DARK MOUNTAIN

DARK MOUNTAIN

REFUGE

TEN YEARS

ON

THE MOUNTAIN

THE DARK MOUNTAIN PROJECT

ISSUE 16 • AUTUMN 2019

Published by the Dark Mountain Project 2019
dark-mountain.net

ISBN 978-0-9955402-7-9

Editors
Charlotte Du Cann
Anthea Lawson
Tom Smith

Poetry editor
Cate Chapman

Art editor
Charlotte Du Cann

Commissioning editors
Nick Hunt
Steve Wheeler

Assistant editor
Philip Webb Gregg

Proofreader
Mark Watson

Editorial assistant
Ava Osbiston

Typesetting
Christian Brett,
Bracketpress

Printed and bound by
TJ International Ltd.,
Padstow, PL28 8RW

Cover art

Jacket design by Christian Brett

Cover: Lead Me to Places I Could Never Find on My Own I (from the series 'As Immense as the Sky')
by Meryl McMaster
Digital C-print

Contemplating time and the countless cycles of life that have recurred around the ancient *mistassini* (monoliths), *sputinas* (buttes), wiyacahk (canyons) and *ayeakow awacha* (dunes) of Turtle Island led to the development of 'As Immense as the Sky'. These thoughts left me in a state of wonderment, but also stirred within me a fearful apprehension of our permanent and collective impact upon our beautiful world. (Courtesy of The Baldwin Gallery)

ISSUE 16 • REFUGE • AUTUMN 2019

Contents

DARK MOUNTAIN • 16

Of Water and Desert

Of Time and Apocalypse

Of Gods and Monsters

Of Rites of Passage

CONTENTS

ROBERT LEAVER

Man Down

Sex shop, Times Square, New York (photo: Teddy Jefferson)

For story see p.81

Editorial

When the Cities Lie at the Monster's Feet There Are Left the Mountains

On the mountain there is a refuge. You stumble upon it on a dark stormy night, when you feel you have lost your way. The door is unlocked, the room is bare but inviting: a table, a bed, a lamp, firewood. It is a space where others have been before you and will come when you have gone. Here you stop, catch your breath and find your bearings. In this rough crucible, as the wind howls outside, you write and sketch, dream and weep. In the morning there comes calm. You are still heading down the hill, but your head is clear and you no longer feel alone.

For ten years the Dark Mountain Project has been a refuge, a lookout point on a precipitous journey of descent. Its territory has always been singular. As much a soberness of mood, a position to take, or a frame of reference, it has created a platform where we can acknowledge that, even as mainstream culture still aspires upward, it is 'time to look down'. From the publication of the manifesto, across 16 books, five festivals, hundreds of online articles and artistic collaborations, the project has provided a space within which to pause, against a twilit backdrop of environmental and social breakdown, and step outside the bubble of civilisation. This space has acted as a gathering point where we can consider the destiny of human and more-than-human collectives – and the planet itself – in the face of decline and ecocide.

The hardback books have always been at the centre of what we do, the project's heartbeat and rhythm. Navigating a territory beyond progress, they log the testimonies of writers and artists confronting the existential and experiential questions about our predicament, in all their beauty, joy and terror. The issue you hold in your hands is a threshold publication. It contains 56 responses to an invitation sent to some of our most seasoned 'mountaineers' – fellow travellers who have walked alongside the project at different twists and turns on its journey, some for the long-haul, some for a brief spell. We invited everyone to reflect on the undercurrents of the last ten years, from the big picture to the microscopic, and then to look at what lies ahead. It marks a pivotal moment, not only in our existence as a project, but also the closing of a tumultuous decade, a decade which has made the refuge provided by Dark Mountain seem more crucial than ever.

When we see that collapse is coming – or is already underway – it is tempting to look for the precise moment when difficulties began, the fork where an erroneous path was taken. Was it industrialisation? No, it was farming. Was it capitalist individualism? No, it was patriarchy. And around we go … Dark Mountain's focus has been to attend to the stories and myths that underpin our human-centric worldview, to ask how our civilisation's ecocidal narrative web has got us into this fatal muddle. Which stories were told that placed us outside and above nature? Which ones detached us from place and its other inhabitants? Which myths took us out of cyclical time and into a continuous line of progress which allows us to think we can search for wrong turnings at all? And which stories might speak to us in an age of endings?

Surprisingly perhaps, for a book that looks back at these turbulent years, there is almost no reference to the chatterings of media headlines or online outrage. You will find little discussion of the demagogues of the age, certainly no mention of Twitter, fake news or the latest iPhone. When you are in that refuge – offline, offgrid – what concerns you is not the latest political scandal, but how resilient you are in ways that are

rarely discussed: in your heart and soul. The question you most consider, as the tempest builds and the creatures disappear, is how can you connect with the Earth that sustains every breath you take? How can you connect with the ancestral knowledge that once instructed us in how to live in beauty and harmony here?

For some in these pages, the wind-rocked bothy is on a literal mountain, Beinn a' Bhric above Rannoch Moor, where Dougie Strang clears the Cailleach's well on the first of May. Or it is a tent on the Bay of Biscay as Catrina Davies ends an epic cycle across Spain, or travelling in a car down a long stretch of Colorado highway in Rob Carney's dystopian ballad. For others, that still point is a state of awakeness in a time of amnesia; the moment of realisation, as Jay Griffiths glides above a dying coral reef in the Indian Ocean, or Anthea Lawson finds herself in a police cell in Wembley, or the narrator in Eric Robertson's story watches as a 'poor dumb bastard' walks towards his death in a feral pasture in Utah.

Our art has always been marked by the dramaturgical, by work that is found or enacted in the cities and in the woods: women put on costumes that reveal their mythic roles, men shed their clothes and immerse themselves in lakewater and snow. After a decade of distance-walking across Europe, Monique Besten heads home dispersing cosmos seeds along the highway; after a decade wearing his father's '60s suit crawling down Broadway, or curled up in holes dug by hand in deserts and clifftops, Robert Leaver ends up face down in a quarry in the Adirondack

mountains. How did they get there? We follow their tracks.

Among all the themes in this book, what connects this great shoal of stories, paintings, photographs, poems, interviews and essays, is the search for a lexicon that not only explores the existential crisis we share, but that might also break us out of a mindset that distorts our perception and keeps us in cultural lockdown. An uncivilised language of body, spirit and imagination, which requires a decolonising of our own Empire vocabulary and the finding of a deeper story about being human. 'How can you possibly tell the story of the world that isn't human?' asks Paul Kingsnorth in conversation with Charlotte Du Cann. 'How do you build a culture which sees the world as a living, sacred community of which you are part?'

Around these pages twines an alphabet of leaves and honeysuckle branches, seabird and river; essays on the elemental and ancestral tellings held in autumn haiku and Arctic string figures. Martin Shaw, writing about the myth-charged wilderness quests he guides, describes the challenges of returning to the village to speak of what has been learned, without words, in the forest. We are so transfixed by the sound of our own voices, Margaret Elphinstone observes, we have become deaf to the voices of creatures and trees. Listen, says the Hare to Deadman in the poem. Open your ears.

At Dark Mountain's 10th anniversary celebration by the river Thames this summer, someone asked us: 'Where will the project be taken from here?' 'Nowhere,' we replied. Because, after a decade on the mountain,

here is where we intend to stay. Our door will remain unlocked, even as the storm increases.

At this threshold, we'd like to thank everyone who has made this creative project happen: all the editors, writers, artists, administrators, collaborators, subscribers and readers. Everyone who has sat around the campfire with us and taken part in our events and publications. Many thanks and fair winds to our co-founders, Paul Kingsnorth and Dougald Hine, who have both now left to venture elsewhere. And many thanks to everyone who has contributed to this anniversary issue and especially to Christian Brett, our typesetter at Bracketpress, who has designed every book we have produced and who created this book's jacket.

See you on the mountain.

The Editors

Dark Mountain would not exist without the support and generosity of its readers. There are many ways to get involved with the project, but the simplest and most direct form of support you can offer is to become a subscriber. For more information, visit: **dark-mountain.net/subscriptions/**

[below and previous spread]

KAHN & SELESNICK
Danses Macabres – Fools and Animals (from the series 'Auguries')

Paul O'Connor

Nightfall in Atlantis

Dubai blues

We walk in an eerie half-light through low rooms whose arched ceilings press down on our heads with an almost physical weight. Behind walls of plate glass, shoals of fish swim among broken columns and tumbled piles of cyclopean masonry. Manta rays sail past like white, flapping ghosts; eels squirm in and out between slabs of stone engraved with indecipherable hieroglyphics. Strange metal contraptions, the relics of a mysterious but advanced technology, litter the rooms. We are looking at the inundated ruins of a great civilisation, one that in its hubris transgressed the limits imposed on it by the gods, was overwhelmed by cataclysm and swallowed by the sea.

My family and I are visiting Atlantis – the Atlantis Hotel, at the tip of the Palm Jumeirah in Dubai, where the Lost Chambers aquarium aims to recreate the atmosphere of the drowned civilisation. My four-year-old twins are fascinated by the fish, and there are limited places to take them in the 40°C heat, so it's worth making the drive across the desert from Al Ain, where I teach at the university. It's even worth suffering the embarrassment of handing over our car, covered in dust and strewn with the detritus of two preschoolers, to the valet who will park it among Range Rovers and Porsches. For my wife, Áine, and myself, there is also the wonder and strangeness of Dubai, which is nearly as alien to our previous life as Atlantis itself.

An hour or so out of Al Ain, it breaks on us, a wall of skyscrapers capped by the near-kilometre-high spire of the Burj Khalifa – a blue-grey mirage condensing out of superheated air. Dubai, with its sprawling shopping malls and Arabian-style McMansions, luxury hotels and labour camps where men sleep six and eight to a room, sleek sports cars and snarling traffic. A city of superlatives: the world's tallest building, the world's largest shopping mall, the world's largest indoor ski-slope, the world's only seven-star hotel (aside from Abu Dhabi's Emirates Palace). All this has been conjured from the desert in only a few decades. If you stand on the viewing platform of the Burj Khalifa, you will see that it is still desert – the flowers and trees planted along the verges of the roads give a false impression of greenery from the ground – and when the wind rises, the air takes on an ochre hue and the skyscrapers are obscured by clouds of sand.

Dubai was rocked by the 2008 financial crisis. As the real estate and tourist markets slumped, the city struggled to pay its debts and had to be bailed out by oil-rich Abu Dhabi. Several of its more ambitious projects, such as Dubai World – a series of artificial islands shaped like a map of the world – were put on hold and have never really taken off again. Today though, it seems to be back in business. Cranes pierce the skyline, tourists cram the *souqs*, and new high-rises are levering themselves upwards.

Dubai's troubles were partly the result of hubris, of overreaching itself: too many mega-projects launched, too much debt taken on. In fact, the very existence of this city in the desert might seem like tempting fate. Hubris too, in a world of rising temperatures and sea levels, to construct a hotel at the end of an artificial peninsula in the Arabian Gulf and name it after Atlantis. But it is easier to condemn Dubai than to look in the mirror it holds up to us all.

After the aquarium, we go for tea and cake in one of the restaurants – decorated with more cyclopean masonry and squat stone pillars that for some reason bring to mind a Mayan temple – and get talking to another expatriate family who have been in Dubai for nine years. The wife is a teacher, her husband works in oilfield services. They complain that the lifestyle in UAE isn't what it was; that salaries are stagnant or declining and the cost of living has gone up. It is a familiar lament. Despite the renewed building and the crowds of tourists, there are constant rumours that the economy is slowing. The region is among the worst impacted by climate change; in the summers, the thermometer often nudges 50°C. Dubai's excesses already have an odour of the ancien régime; its unabashed decadence no longer chimes with the zeitgeist. For the moment, though, the façade of normality is maintained. After all, Atlantis is only a myth. The hieroglyphics in the aquarium propound no warnings, and plate glass protects us from the manta rays and sharks.

Ghost ideas

> 'As I said, the Big Bosses, ay,' his voice sank almost to a whisper, 'ay, even the Biggest, can make mistakes. Something nearly slipped, you say. I say, something *has* slipped. And we've got to look out.'
>
> – J. R. R. Tolkien, *The Lord of the Rings*

Something slipped in 2008. For a few weeks, the global financial system trembled on the brink of meltdown, and with it the entire global economy. International trade fell further and faster than at the start of the Great Depression in 1929. It is 2008, rather than the arbitrary date of 2010, which marks the break between the relatively carefree noughties and our past decade of anxiety. On the one hand, collapse was averted; central banks and governments pulled every lever and played every conjuring trick they could think of to keep the world economy functioning. On the other, business as usual has never quite resumed. The result has been a strange, twilit era in which people continue to recite many of the old mantras and perform the old routines, but without conviction. The bankruptcy of the old world has been revealed, but no new world has yet heaved into view.

This was the decade in which ecological breakdown changed from future threat to present reality. Seven of the ten hottest years on record have occurred since 2010. Droughts worsened by climate change contributed to the civil turmoil of the Arab Spring and the refugee crisis in Europe. Warning signals of the destruction of life on Earth are flashing everywhere: 40% of insect species globally are in decline; the number of flying insects in nature reserves across Germany plunged by three-quarters in 25 years; the number of moths in the UK has declined by two-thirds since 1968. These signs of imminent catastrophe have prompted a surge of public concern. But at the end of the decade, the fossil-fuelled, growth-orientated, consumption-driven model of economy and society remains fundamentally unchanged. In 2017 and 2018, global carbon emissions started to rise again after a three-year pause; in the latter year, 80% of global energy demand was met by coal, oil and gas, according to the International Energy Agency, a percentage unchanged since 2000.

Yet this was also the decade when the growth-based economic model ceased to deliver, even in its own narrow terms. Whatever the headline figures for economic growth, the reality for most people under 40 has been one of stagnant wages, persistent indebtedness, work which is becoming more precarious, stressful and demeaning, and housing which is impossibly expensive either to rent or buy. In Western societies, at least, the great surge in living standards which shaped the decades after the Second World War has stalled and gone into reverse.

Consequently, this was a decade when governments nearly everywhere suffered a crisis of legitimacy. The post-war social contract, which secured broad acceptance of the capitalist system through redistribution of the wealth it generated – already undermined by neoliberalism – has now virtually collapsed. The result is a rejection of political elites, which has manifested itself in the rise of populism and strongman leaders around the world, from the United States to the Philippines and from Turkey to Brazil. Yet, a striking characteristic of populist movements – whether of the right or left – is that their political imaginary is driven not by new ideas but by a desire to return to some idealised past. For populists of the right, this is a sovereign, ethnically homogeneous nation state; for populists of the left, it is a revamped version of the post-war welfare state. Politics today is driven not by hope for a brighter future but by nostalgia for a more secure world. Political parties still battle beneath the moth-eaten banners of industrial-era ideologies – socialism, liberalism, nationalism – that have had increasingly little relevance to the actual conditions of developed societies since the 1970s.

Finally, this was the decade when the utopian hopes invested in digital technology as the harbinger of a new wave of democratisation, gave way to more dystopian vistas. The launch of Facebook in 2004 and the iPhone in 2007 can be seen as inaugurating a period when the internet ceased being one communication medium among many, and became the matrix of social life, the water in which we swim. Since then, the digitalisation of everyday living has reached a critical mass. Digital technology is rewiring our brains and changing our perceptions of what counts as reality, while providing governments and corporations with new tools for surveillance and control (with China's social credit system a foretaste of the kind of horrors that may await us). Is it a coincidence that as real life has become bleaker, virtual life has effloresced? In the future, as challenges to the legitimacy of the political system deepen, technology is likely to play a central role in efforts to maintain it, both as a direct tool of social control and through the virtual world providing compensation for the stresses of the real one.

What all this adds up to is a decade when old certainties about progress, growth, markets, welfare, democracy and the capacity of professional knowledge and bureaucratic action to solve social problems were eroded, but no new narrative emerged to replace them. Instead, the old myths live on in the ever-more hollow utterances of establishment politicians, the platitudes of newspaper columnists and talking heads, and the jaded recommendations of think tanks and academics. They have been joined, not by new ideas, but by ghosts supposed to have been buried with the last century: the siren calls of ethnic hatred and great power competition, and would-be strongmen strutting and posturing like an old newsreel of Mussolini. In everyday life, meanwhile, we go about our habitual routines, except that our wages don't stretch quite as far as before, we are a little more anxious about the future, less secure in our jobs, less assured of maintaining a roof over our heads, and have less faith in both the ability of government to represent us and experts to solve our problems.

Everyday insanity

> No live organism can continue for long to exist sanely under conditions of absolute reality; even larks and katydids are supposed, by some, to dream.
>
> – Shirley Jackson, *The Haunting of Hill House*

Contemporary civilisation is the end result of a long line of opportunity traps: the shift from hunting and gathering to agriculture, the intensification of agriculture in the river valleys of the Nile and Mesopotamia, the transposition of European civilisation to the Americas, the exploitation of coal during the Industrial Revolution, the use of oil to power a globally integrated economic order. Each step initially promised a better standard of living, but ultimately led to an expanded population, greater strain on the Earth's resources, and an increase in social complexity which reduced the autonomy of individuals. We are now reaching a point where the environmental damage caused by growth is piling up sufficiently to ricochet back on society and reduce the prospects of future growth. Higher extraction costs and lower quality of natural resources, as well as the rising tempo of natural disasters, are undoubtedly part of the reason for the underperformance of the global economy over the past decade. The social costs of economic growth are piling up as well: widening inequality, societal atomisation, inter-group conflict, declining trust in institutions, depression, stress, anxiety. But our civilisation understands only the logic of an expanding economy and growing societal complexity. An economy which cannot function without growth, and a state apparatus which has enjoyed continual increases in disciplinary control over its citizens for nearly 500 years, are incapable of facilitating an orderly step-down to a more sustainable level of existence.

But the challenges of a society in overshoot cannot be solved using the logic of the system which created them. Take the current 'energy transition', driven by bureaucratic mandates, corporate investment and industrial-scale technologies. Although spun as 'green', the outcome of this drive to create a low-carbon energy infrastructure will not be the protection of landscapes and biodiversity, but industrialisation of the countryside. Not community energy, but industrial-scale wind and solar arrays run by corporate behemoths. Not public transport and walkable streets, but the replication of our current unsustainable and socially atomising car culture in electric format. Not individual autonomy, but deeper integration into the system through smart technologies that regulate the consumption of resources. The future we are offered by corporate and governmental 'sustainability leaders' is the polar opposite of that dreamt of by the old greens, with their permaculture gardens, rooftop solar panels and well-thumbed copies of Ivan Illich.

Nor will it work. So long as growth is sacrosanct, attempts to ease one ecological problem will almost inevitably lead to the worsening of others. We may reduce our dependency on fossil fuels, but at the cost of biodiversity, as tropical rainforest is cut down to make way for palm oil plantations and mountains and moorland are covered in wind farms. We may purchase ourselves a few extra years by delaying global warming, so we can spend them deep-trawling the oceans and paving over farmland with new suburbs. Moreover, so long as we operate within a cultural framework dominated by technological solutionism and bureaucratic management, every effort to address environmental or social problems will involve some new layer of bureaucracy, some new set of regulations, some new deployment of technology. This runs slap into the dilemma identified by Joseph Tainter: civilisations are problem-solving mechanisms and they solve problems through developing new layers of complex organisation. This complexity generates new problems of its own; over time, the rising costs and declining marginal returns on complexity mean life for most ordinary inhabitants of the civilisation becomes unbearable; they revolt or flee, and the civilisation collapses.

The UAE is an extreme example of the dilemmas faced by a society in overshoot. Before the discovery of oil, no more than 10,000 people were scattered across the emirate of Abu Dhabi. The populations of the other emirates were even smaller. Bedouin tribes scratched a living from the harsh environment by combining the resources of different ecoregions: fishing and pearling on the coast, the cultivation of date palms in the oases, camel herding in the desert. The past half-century has seen the country's population explode to almost ten million. Sprawling cities have risen from the sand, cities in which life is only made possible by 24-hour air conditioning and water from desalination plants. Virtually all food is imported. Stepping down from this to a more localised and sustainable mode of living is hardly an option. It is no wonder that the UAE seems to be one of the last places on Earth to passionately believe in the myth of progress, even to the point of aiming to establish a colony on Mars by 2117.

So modern society is stuck attempting to solve a proliferating range of problems by applying the same kind of logic that caused them. This may be the definition of insanity, but for many people madness may seem a better option than facing reality. Hence, in the coming decade, the everyday insanity of our world is likely to continue – stuttering economic growth purchased at an ever-increasing environmental and social cost; at least one severe recession; stagnant wages and living standards for the majority; continued prosperity for the 1%; a deepening crisis of legitimacy for democratic states; new populisms of both right and left; more failed states, primarily in North Africa and the Middle East, but not confined to that region; even larger movements of refugees; increased great-power competition, with the strong likelihood of at least one major international conflict; even deeper digitalisation of everyday life; an expansion of corporate and state surveillance and control. There is also likely to be a major effort across the wealthier countries to roll out more 'sustainable' infrastructure – renewable energy, electric cars, smart grids and energy-efficient buildings – but it is debatable whether this will lead to a reduction in carbon emissions anywhere near enough to avert catastrophic climate change. The public discourse of the decade will feature the usual obligatory optimism, and leaders will come and go talking about hope and change, but in 2030 most people will be a little poorer than today and live somewhat more insecure and precarious lives. Happily, however, they will have even greater facilities for digital distraction than we do now.

Total closure

> Then the whole system becomes weightless, it is no longer anything but a gigantic simulacrum – not unreal, but simulacrum, that is to say never exchanged for the real, but exchanged for itself, in an uninterrupted circuit without reference or circumference.
>
> – Jean Baudrillard, *Simulcra and Simulation*

My wife often describes our life in the UAE as being like the Big Brother house. What she's getting at is our sense of the unreality of life here, and how inconsequential most of what we do or experience seems. It is a life so air-conditioned and aseptic that it feels like we inhabit a bubble whose impermeable skin is always between us and reality. For nearly half the year it is impossible to stay outdoors for more than a few minutes without feeling heat sick. Shopping malls are the closest thing to public space, and the main leisure activity seems to be visiting them. People venture onto the roads in masses of metal more suitable for the Eastern Front circa 1943 than a trip to Carrefour. There are few paths, and Áine gave up her attempts to go for a walk after anxious locals stopped repeatedly to ask her if she needed a lift.

A lot of the time, it's as though we've stumbled onto a film set, confused extras unsure of our part. There was the beach in Abu Dhabi where everyone seemed like a refugee from Love Island, all bronzed bikini bodies, waxed torsos and tattoos of Chinese ideograms. The global village in Dubai, with its one-dimensional mock-ups of the Taj Mahal, the pyramids of Giza and the Colosseum that look like Hollywood backdrops. The crowds waving selfie sticks on top of the Burj Khalifa. The acquaintance who marked her 40th birthday by hiring a photographer to take pictures of herself posing like a glamour model in the desert, then shared them on Facebook. The students at my university getting plastic surgery before they are 20. Life only exists insofar as it's photographed, recorded, uploaded, shared, liked and imitates what has already been photographed, recorded, uploaded, shared and liked by others.

The ultimate opportunity trap is the success of our civilisation in controlling its environment, managing risk, and translating everything extrinsic to it into its own terms of monetary value, instrumental rationality and mediatised entertainment. In a way without precedent in any human culture of the past, our civilisation has achieved almost total closure against anything external to its own version of reality. Whatever cannot be translated into these terms is either invisible or delegitimised, cast as fantasy or nonsense. Hence, for example, it is almost impossible within mainstream discourse to talk of the natural world as having intrinsic value. Rivers and forests, butterflies and bees, must be given an economic price tag or an instrumental function as providers of 'ecosystem services' in order to be worth preserving. This is not to say our civilisation has achieved independence of its ecological underpinnings. What it does mean is that the facilities for ignoring them are practically inexhaustible.

There is something more fundamental going on here than the preponderance of economic logic or quantitative thinking. It is the refusal to recognise as real anything outside a narrow socially constructed and mediated horizon of experience; the refusal to recognise our existential status as embodied organisms with an intrinsic connection to the Earth, a kinship with animals, an emotional response to the landscape and seasons; to recognise our status as mortals who will inevitably age and die, but who also participate in the natural cycles of regeneration and rebirth. This way of thinking has deep roots in Western civilisation. They go back to Judaic monotheism, which stripped the natural world of its sacred aura, transferring it to the abstract, transcendent figure of a single god; and Greek rationalism, with its elevation of the disembodied forms of Platonic ideas over the sensual chaos of concrete life. Both these traditions were revitalised at the birth of the modern age, fundamentally shaping its character. Calvinistic Protestantism took the devaluation of the living Earth and sensual life in favour of an utterly transcendent god to pathological extremes; while the scientific worldview codified by Descartes and Bacon privileged conceptual thought over lived experience, denied the universe any intrinsic value or meaning, and envisaged nature as a dead and soulless mechanism.

If the physical world had no intrinsic value, it could be exploited, destroyed, manipulated and repurposed without guilt. Calvinism and Cartesianism provided the cultural underpinnings for the rise of capitalism and the scientific revolution. Industry and technology in turn empowered humanity to remake its habitat to an unprecedented degree. We have sealed ourselves off from the other-than-human world. Dubai, with its ski slopes in the desert, artificial islands and peninsulas, and maze-like shopping centres which confuse the sense of direction and suspend the sense of time, simply gives more extravagant expression to the logic in which we are entrapped. This self-containment is not just physical or virtual, but intellectual and emotional. The habitat we have created is thus not neutral, but encodes the values of Cartesian rationalism and the Calvinistic work ethic which underlie modern society: the absolute separation between humanity and nature; the denial of any intrinsic value to a natural world conceived as a passive substrate which humanity can manipulate at will; the worship of technology as a source of power and human control; the belief in work – even mindless, purposeless activity – as an end in itself. Modern civilisation has extruded a physical carapace, like a crab growing its shell, which embodies and encodes its underlying logic. The strange conviction that exponential growth is possible on a finite planet – that it is indeed our God-given right and entitlement – is at least partly due to our increasingly total immersion in a social construct which, even in its most physical manifestations, represents the crystallisation of an abstraction.

A central insight of both Nietzsche and Max Weber was that the 'spirit' of modern society had its roots in religious and philosophical movements of the ancient world which were inherently 'world-rejecting', and which sacrificed sensual, concrete life to fictitious and abstract values. The weakening of institutional religion in the modern world did not lead to the rejection of these values, but their reinforcement, in the form of secular translations like the work ethic or scientific rationalism and the worship of technology. This is the basis of Nietzsche's diagnosis of Western nihilism; we inhabit a culture which prefers its own illusions to concrete life. Of all modern myths, the one our culture clings to most tenaciously is the myth of human control. Perhaps it would even prefer oblivion to letting this myth go; hence the ever-deepening strain of nihilism in contemporary society. The result is a civilisation which wallows in simulation and dissimulation, denial and distraction, smoke and mirrors, cargo-cult behaviours, nihilistic violence, fantasy and self-delusion, even as its ecological underpinnings start to give way.

It was the father of the current ruler of Dubai who, reflecting on the precarity of oil wealth, said 'My grandfather rode a camel, my father rode a camel, I drive a Mercedes, my son drives a Land Rover, his son will drive a Land Rover, but his son will ride a camel.' I am the first person in my family to have a university degree and a middle-class job. I often wonder if I will also be the last. Whenever I hear those around us expound on the virtues of the private schools attended by their children, I think a few acres of good land back in Ireland might give my son and daughter a better assurance of the future. Yet where we stand, all paths are fraught with peril. Before Atlantis sank under the waves, people must have felt the tremors of the approaching earthquake. But if Atlantis is our whole world, what lifeboats can we build, or what safe harbours are there to sail to?

Nina Pick

Seducing the Moon

The deep-voiced narrator of the nature programme tells us
that according to the ancient mythology of the region
hummingbirds were created to seduce the moon
which we can certainly believe
the lashes of their wings opening and closing flirtatiously
glistening like the blue heart of flame in the stark Andean light
the kind of light that opens our bodies like ripe oranges
and sticks its teeth in
as the azure-winged butterflies emerge from the chrysalis
and the world's most poisonous frog unfurls its gelatinous tongue
while we watch Netflix holding hands in bed in our small apartment
just north of New York City as the sunflowers I recently planted
grow in the dark in the rain like a secret prayer
for the continuity of it all

Akshay Ahuja

Invasives

Until recently, I worked at an unusual private foundation – part woodland, part farm, part centre for the arts – which used an outsize portion of its endowment to combat one family of invasive plants: *Lonicera maackii* and *Lonicera tatarica,* or Amur and Tatarian bush honeysuckle. Once planted as ornamentals, these plants have spread across the American Midwest until they have taken over the understory of many smaller patches of forest.

Tools frowned upon in the organisation's other activities were acceptable if used against this particular enemy: herbicides, bulldozers, fume-spewing chippers. Swarms of volunteers, eager to reconnect with nature (or forced to do so, in the case of some students), were encouraged to achieve this communion by uprooting plants and sawing into honeysuckle trunks. Professionals would come by later and paint the exposed wood with glyphosate.

All of this was done in the name of restoring the woodland to its original purity. After the clearings, triumphal pictures were sent out of native wildflowers, lifting up lovely heads after years under the thickets. Nothing was planted in the bare areas, so honeysuckle would naturally show up again in a few years, or sometimes resprout immediately from the roots.

Nature-oriented organisations throughout the region were busy with this task, and no amount of volunteer time seemed to be sufficient. Every cleared section of forest had to be monitored for fresh plants, all while honeysuckle continued taking over new areas.

The long battle had engendered a kind of hatred. Highly moral language was deployed from people who were, in other circumstances, gently mystical about nature finding its own balance, or blandly scientific about species migrating in response to climate change. Honeysuckle, though, was in its own category – it was simply a bad plant. Leaves appeared early in spring and dropped late in winter, robbing other plants of the sunlight that, after so many years of evolution, they surely had a right to expect. Birds ate the berries and spread the seeds – otherwise the plant would not be so successful – but the honeysuckle berries were sugary, I was told, not *truly* nutritious, the equivalent of junk food. Yes, this duplicitous bush was *tricking* the birds into eating its berries! Like us, it seems birds need coaching and strict restraints to arrive at a healthy and moral diet.

Honeysuckle rather seemed to relish the conflict itself. Bushes would respond to cuts with more gnarled, luxuriant growth, impeding the progress of any ungainly upright animals who wanted to move through the space. The plant also has what I would describe as a sense of humour. Every American child knows, or at least once knew, how to suck the drop of sweetness at the base of a honeysuckle flower. Nope. Wrong plant. Only the larger flowers on *Lonicera* vines are sweet; those on invasive bush honeysuckle don't taste like much of anything. Then, later in summer, the imposter's beautiful red berries send out every signal of human deliciousness but are as bitter as can be imagined on the tongue. For months, the mocking dots of red poke thickly out of the forests, just at our height.

A few months ago, my son was having terrible nightmares and I read Ann Sayre Wiseman's two books on dreams. When Wiseman worked with children, she would suggest that they draw the monsters which were stalking them at night, and then ask, what should we do about this? How can we solve this problem? Sometimes the children would suggest shooting or killing the monster. This particular solution, Wiseman notes, never works. The monster always comes back.

So does honeysuckle.

After an extensive bout of removal, as I looked at the carnage on the forest floor from both bulldozers and human uprooting, I started to wonder whether any of this was worthwhile – or, at least, whether it was the best way to spend huge sums of money and volunteer time. When I suggested planting trees on some of the foundation's many lawns, though, the leadership had serious reservations. Too much maintenance, I was told.

Maintenance – even endless maintenance – is acceptable, I discovered, but only in the service of a holding pattern, the forest as it used to be. Time spent watching an emerging order and responding to it, maybe with some gentle guidance – well, that's risky, too open-ended.

There is a word for a piece of land that cannot maintain its shape without our constant involvement and which makes almost no decisions for itself. The word is garden.

I like gardens. I have a small one. In a garden, we get to talk a lot about what we want. As we move farther from our plot, though, we have fewer decisions to make. Keep walking towards the trees and the presences grow larger. They don't demand silence but it is certainly encouraged. Even talkative children, walking into a forest, get a little quieter. Be quiet long enough and you start to receive something. Communications.

Here are some of the messages we received.

Honeysuckle branches, piled up, take ages to biodegrade. The usual solution is to chip the stuff, which is what the organisation did. But chipped honeysuckle discourages the growth of many other plants. What first came back at the sunny edges of clearings, the human entrance points, were things like poison ivy and hemlock, a small piece of which, consumed, will kill a person or a livestock animal.

Then, the spring after the honeysuckle removal, there was an explosion of ticks on the farm. They fell from the trees and latched on from the tall grass. I was constantly finding them on myself and on the children who came for field trips. My friend suggested that deer were abandoning the areas without a honeysuckle understory – this is where the mothers keep their fauns as they browse – and the ticks were fanning out, looking for new hosts.

Two people on the farm contracted Lyme disease, which conventional medicine finds increasingly difficult to treat.

When a forest, or any group of living things, is ignored for long enough, while also being constantly meddled with, it starts to speak more loudly, with sharper edges. The dream monsters return every night, and they start to bring friends. Eventually, the messages get fierce enough that even the marginally attuned can hear them.

This is what I heard the forest saying.

I feel unsettled, much more than usual.
Something deep and serious is changing
So I am changing too. I am on my way somewhere
To a new integrity.
You should know: it won't look the same as the old one.
I am using what is available to me.

This plant that you brought here is part of this.
So are you.
We are on this journey together.
Be still. Then, if you must move,
Move gently.
Find your place within these changes.

I had planned to write about where our literature has gone in the years since Dark Mountain began. I am perhaps no longer the person to do this. I don't read many new books, and I read far fewer old books than I used to. I am, in many ways, in the state of the forest that I describe above, crawling on the edges with invasives that I no longer know how to control.

Most forests in the United States are damaged. They were cleared at some point for farm, pasture or timber, and still carry the story of these wounds. Almost all of the established trees are the same size and age, quite young, and only belong to a few species. The patches are too fragmented, cut up by roads and development. These are the woodlands most susceptible to invasives.

In any living system, a dangerous and unstable vitality is preferred to impoverishment.

The nearest old-growth forest is several hours' drive away from me, in Indiana. I would like to go there someday. If I find the old wholeness, and can still recognise it, I will be very quiet and wait to see what it might say. But right now my neighbours are these patches of young trees and bush honeysuckle. They are what I have to work with, and I am part of what they have to work with.

What we do to the land, we do to our own imaginations. In the forests of our stories too, behind some energy and a few flashes of beauty, there is a hidden sameness that indicates some previous clear-cut, ideological or quite literal. None of this, of course, has changed substantially over the past decade.

What has changed is the presence, on the borders, of the invasives. These creatures can smell weakness and ill-health at an enormous distance. They cluster around sores. The keepers don't have the energy or resources to control them anymore and suddenly they are everywhere. So they are acknowledged now – but only as a threat, as something outside the real conversation, the true forest. Honeysuckle. Autumn olive. Lesser celandine. Strange, sturdy, tricky little monsters that seem to thrive better than the natives. Each time the guardians of our culture cut or spray them out, they regenerate in more durable and often poisonous forms.

Fresh arguments must be put forth, or old ones repeated. Look – they lack the grandeur of what once grew here. They destroy the health of the whole place. They spread like some kind of disease. And they somehow trick people, like those honeysuckle berries, into using them for sustenance and spreading them elsewhere. The question of why the current landscape isn't providing adequate sustenance is rarely asked.

For a long time, even after I began writing for Dark Mountain, I would have identified myself as one of these guardians. My general pattern was using some piece of old culture as a stick with which to beat new culture – *Here*, I would say, pounding away, *this is what integrity actually looks like. This is how you can recognise these frauds.*

Something happened a few years ago, though. Much as it did in the middle of my single day removing honeysuckle, I completely lost my confidence in the usefulness of this particular job. I wasn't sure the forest needed this kind of help.

The young people I worked with, I noticed, also did not need such guardians. They were quite mixed up, with all sorts of seemingly incompatible ideas, native and foreign, traditional and newfangled, but they did not feel themselves to be damaged or requiring cleansing. Instead, using materials close at hand, they were working towards a new coherence. They hadn't needed to spend years freeing themselves from conventionality, and had used this time to become significantly more competent than me at everything I now thought important. And like the surrounding patches of forest, I could sense that they were on their way to becoming something else, a mixed-up-ness in the process of building its own integrity. And they were much closer to being rooted and healthy than I was.

I felt worthless for a while, fumbling with leaky hoses, nearly passing out placing squash transplants in the heat, not knowing the names of many common birds or trees. In three years, I wrote nothing that wasn't for a paycheck. I didn't feel like I was in possession of knowledge that merited anyone's attention. Many books turned strange on my shelf. Some were dead; others, I could tell, were just going dormant for a while, like trees facing the winter.

I have come out of the transition confused, but with plenty of work still to do. And I know what kinds of books have survived; they are among the few that I could recommend to the young people on the farm, and tellingly, none of them is likely to receive a review in the official places. These are all recombinant ecosystems – not possessing a deep stability or integrity, like the old forms, but touch a finger to their wrists and you will feel a strong pulse, not a weakening one.

Some of the best of them are books of skills, how-to books, where philosophy mingles with more practical matters – books that aren't generally considered literature at all. Masanobu Fukuoka and Euell Gibbons' books are like this. As is Samuel Thayer's great trilogy of books on foraging, with their essays on ecology combined with detailed plant accounts, along with instructions on how to process and cook wild food. Or Harlan Hubbard's memoir and sketchbook, *Payne Hollow*, detailing a life lived mostly on a half-hidden bend of a river.

One might ask, how can a piece of writing be great if it deals with something like temperate-climate North American plants, or with information that is mostly interesting to people in a particular bioregion? Shouldn't great literature be more universal?

Not necessarily. I think some part should always remain inaccessible to outsiders. I have always loved the English poet Edward Thomas, but I realise that I can never know a poem like 'Old Man or Lad's Love' at the same depth as a person who has lived with the plant that he is writing about *(Artemisia abrotanum)* and has known its smell from childhood. A recent Wendell Berry poem about Joe-Pye weed – or, for that matter, this entire essay! – might encounter a similar limit with you.

I say good. We have been too comprehensible to each other for too long. Let us be strange again. There is no love without some distance. Much of my response to ancient Chinese poetry or old Scottish folk songs is based on their mysteriousness, on what I am sure are many profound misunderstandings.

Thayer publishes his books through his own company, along with preserves made from wild food. Hubbard's memoir, the manuscript of which was almost lost (there was one copy), is now printed by a little Kentucky press. These are not conventional models of how to share books or make a living. I have noticed with joy the tenacious survival of presses like the one that keeps Hubbard's book alive, all while breaking every rule of how to succeed in the modern world. My local bookstore told me Hubbard's book was out of print. The publisher, Gnomon, said I just needed to mail them some money and they would send it to me. Places like this, I suspect, will keep cranking on their letterpresses as the civilisations pass.

Payne Hollow (its subtitle, fittingly, is *Life on the Fringe of Society*) conforms to no particular genre. It is memoir, sketchbook, philosophy, gentle invective, and also a decent guide to river-bottom gardening and goat care in this particular climate, should you be interested. Genres are like forests too. We need to notice when they are unhealthy and welcome something new, even if it seems, at first, as raw and amateurish as the shantyboat on which Hubbard and his wife Anna lived for many years.

I am not, of course, telling anyone what kind of writing is worth doing. I have just noticed many people, myself included, writing novels and poems who do not really want to be writing novels or poems. They are trying to squeeze some not-yet-categorisable utterance into an old form, simply because it seems like what serious writing is supposed to look like.

Writing is not supposed to look like anything. Forests are not supposed to look like anything. Not any more. Things are changing too fast.

There is a farm down the road from me, partially tended by refugees from Bhutan. The Bhutanese have a large garden of their own where they grow native varieties of crops. The farmer, of course, had engaged in a recent bout of honeysuckle removal, and the trunks and branches were lying around in piles.

The Bhutanese asked – can we use them? Of course, they were told – it's just waste material.

They picked up the wood. They must have noticed its fibrousness (honeysuckle bends, but doesn't tend to snap), its strange resistance to decay.

A few months later, when I went to visit their garden, walls and trellises had risen up in profusion. Using the abandoned honeysuckle branches, the Bhutanese had built a whole garden city of narrow alleyways and tiny enclosures, with plots of corn and chillies and marigolds. Honeysuckle branches are almost never straight, so all around me, sometimes rising 12 feet into the air, were curving turrets of wood, each waving green with the vines of squash and beans.

It was the most gorgeous and exuberant vegetable garden I have ever seen, with its bones entirely built out of honeysuckle. Back at the foundation, we were getting much worse results using the ugliness of T-posts and hoops and plastic and row cover. I was too enchanted, though, to feel ashamed. These farmers – foreigners, non-natives – had seen the truth. Anything that grows with such tenacity is not a pest to be eradicated but a gift to be used. And, eventually – as we listen to it and speak with it over generations – a gift to be used with increasing skill and beauty.

The nightmare monsters cannot be killed. To kill something, Wiseman says, is just another way of ignoring it. Nor can we simply let the monsters do as they please until our lives are intolerable. They are here for a reason; they are a message. Once we realise this, and listen, the conversation can begin.

Coppice – some light clearing – trellis-building. We can make these statements. They are polite, not at all like bulldozers and poison sprays. What do you think, honeysuckle? Then, every so often, we can stop talking and wait for our turn again. What do the birds have to say? How about the ticks and the mosquitoes?

It will need to be a long conversation – like literature, headed both somewhere and nowhere. And for a while, it won't be beautiful. It will seem like a mess. But it is the mess we are in, and there is no other place for us to be.

Charlotte Du Cann

The Earth Does Not Speak in Prose

A conversation with Paul Kingsnorth

In 2008, Paul Kingsnorth was working on two seismic texts. One was a small red pamphlet, engineered with fellow ex-journalist Dougald Hine, that laid down the tracks for what would become the Dark Mountain Project; the other was a post-apocalyptic novel written in a 'shadow tongue', the first in a trilogy of books that follows the fate of a man on the brink of collapse in different millennia. Both make strong demands on the reader. *Uncivilisation* challenges a world view conventionally shaped by progress, technology and human exceptionalism; *The Wake*, our linguistic skills and capacity to step into the mindset of someone whose land, culture and sense of being in control is taken away by a force outside their known boundaries.

In 2019, I am sitting opposite the writer who has for the last decade wrestled with these crises in essays, fiction and poetry; who has shaped anthologies, directed festivals and writing courses and brought together a collection of writers and artists to pay attention to the ecological and social collapse we all inevitably face. I realise that despite having worked alongside each other during these years, we have never spoken about our mutual craft, and that now is the moment. We are in a coffee shop in the bookish town of Hay-on-Wye. It's midsummer, a golden day in the Golden Valley. In his just-published non-fiction work, *Savage Gods*, he challenges himself: on his quest to find a place to belong on the Earth, and on his true worth as a wielder of words. Finally he is thrown the gauntlet by the mischievous god Loki, who, swiping a beer from his fridge, tells him to 'shut up' entirely.

Luckily for you and me, this only refers to writing…

CDC Looking back at the decade, from the time of the manifesto to now, what strikes you as most significant in terms of the zeitgeist?

PK Perhaps the most significant fact about the last decade is how much was said in the manifesto that has become pretty much widely accepted. In terms of the culture, it was quite a wild thing to be saying: that it is not possible to stop the collapse and that we need to write about the situation for real.

Now the kind of things we were publishing in the first books you can find in the *New York Times* and the *Guardian*; in the fact that Extinction Rebellion are called Extinction Rebellion. Most people are saying: we are in the catastrophe now, ecologically speaking. Which is a shame because it would have been nice if we had been entirely wrong.

CDC The manifesto threw down a gauntlet for writers and artists to respond to this catastrophe. How successful do you think that has been?

PK Funnily enough, I think that might be the least successful part of Dark Mountain. I had this idea originally that I could found a writer's group like C.S. Lewis and Tolkien, sitting around in the pub talking about orcs, and we would have a little journal. It was Dougald's idea to publish a manifesto so people would know what we were talking about, and he knew all about crowdfunding, which was new at the time.

For me it was a literary project partly because I wanted to get away from being an activist. I largely failed to do that, because I couldn't stop writing about the failure of activism and detach myself from the political conversation. Like George Orwell, I was being constantly pulled between: 'I want to be a literary writer' and 'I've got to get involved in the world I'm in'.

CDC In these ten years, the responses to the manifesto have attracted a certain kind of writing that you wouldn't necessarily call literary...

PK The difference between *Uncivilisation* and, say, the modernist manifestos which partly inspired it, is that we weren't suggesting people should write in a certain way. We were talking about tackling a certain set of themes, particularly demolishing the myth of progress and stepping outside our humanness, taking the crisis seriously and understanding where we are.

The most significant thing turned out to be the non-fiction and maybe the events, and the creation of a group of people who share that perspective.

CDC Maybe the function of writing now is that it can address a territory that activism never really looks at, which is the existential crisis that we're in.

PK In some ways it's not a time for literature. What we call literature is completely inadequate, particularly metropolitan, middle-class British literature that is utterly unconcerned with the great existential issues of our time. That's one of the things that motivated me to write *Savage Gods*: what kind of writing would you produce in this time if you took this seriously? It's not just a question about subject matter, it's a question about form. And it's also a question about why you would even write anything.

CDC So where does that leave the role of the writer, do you suppose?

PK When we wrote the manifesto, I believed very strongly in the writer as an agent of change. And I'm not sure I do anymore. That's part of the crisis that led me to *Savage Gods*: writing about losing faith in the written word. And that's because for me, direct experience is becoming more and more important than experience filtered through writing.

I don't have the same belief that I had ten years ago in the idea that a literary movement of people could produce world-changing stuff. Partly because society is so big and so complex, and when I look back at the manifesto now, I was approaching literature from quite an activist-y mindset. You know, *We will use writing to change the future!*

CDC I really enjoyed the references in *Savage Gods* to people who would definitely be considered writers of literature, such as Yeats or Kavanagh or D.H. Lawrence. Those writers appear like touchstones, like a lineage. Would you describe it like that?

PK I didn't really consciously think about that when I was younger, but I do now. Who would be in my lineage? Yeats would be in my lineage, and Ted Hughes, Jeffers and D.H. Lawrence, Emily Bronte, Wordsworth, and basically all the great dark Romantics. But also others like Orwell, Chesterton, Huxley. There's a certain strain of English radicalism that appeals to me which is quite particular. Now that I've said that, I'll contradict it by talking about lots of American writers…

CDC Robinson Jeffers is not very English…

PK Yes, there's that great American wilderness tradition: Jeffers, but also Thoreau, Edward Abbey. And other writers like Wendell Berry… There's something about American writing about nature and place which appeals to me much more than the kind of polite, middle-class,

Oxbridge-y English nature writing which I find tiresome. I would much rather read someone with this great eagle's perspective on the world.

CDC That is dictated by the land itself, I think.

PK I think it is. Because it's a very small, very old part of the country here in England. Whereas in America you can still stride out, and maybe get killed by a bear, and have a non-human experience at scale.

So if I had a lineage, there's a certain English radical Romantic tradition and there's an American wild landscape tradition. And then also politically, I think of someone like, say, Subcomandante Marcos of the Zapatistas, who was a massive influence on me. Someone who came out of the city and decided to learn about what it meant to be indigenous, to belong to a place and become a revolutionary leader of a very different kind. Firstly, one who's directed by the people themselves. And secondly, one who's coming from a sense of place and culture, which is not an unchanging, reactionary sort of everything-was-viable-in-the-old-days-and-we'll-keep-it-like-that notion. Quite the opposite: the Zapatistas want change. But it's entirely untheoretical.

CDC There seems to be a thread throughout all these writers from Marcos to Wendell Berry: that their work comes out of knowing places, it doesn't come out of the mind.

PK Yes, this something I come back to again and again in all of my writing. The fact that the global machine which is destroying the Earth flourishes by destroying all cultures, all peoples, all places – like grubbing up an orchard. As it ploughs through the world everybody is pulled into the engine to feed the growth machine. And so the process of rooting becomes a radical act but also a difficult one. Because what does that mean when everyone is moving around, if I don't belong anywhere?

The best places I've been in the world in my view have been the most rooted places, where cultures are very old and people have a strong kind of solidity to them, like old trees. And they know their land, and they know it's where their ancestors are buried and where they're going to be buried. Compare that to the kind of weird rootlessness of the modern West, of which I'm a part, and there's no comparison, in terms of the way that people live well.

Most of us aren't living like that. I'm not living like that. And there are more and more people moving around all the time, and migrating and being displaced, some of them voluntarily and some of them not.

That's what we're all doing all the time, internally and externally. How do you get from here to there is the question.

CDC And it's not just a matter of finding your place. It's a matter of having a relationship with that place, whether you 'own' it or not.

PK The reality is that people need to belong across space and time. We need to have a sense of who we are as a people, whatever that means to us, and who our ancestors are. Otherwise we're just individualists. We need a sense of being part of something across time. And we also need a sense of being able to say 'This is my home.' It doesn't have to be where you've come from, but it's the place you are, where you've said, 'This is where I've put my feet down.'

If you look at that from a non-human perspective, it starts to make a lot more sense. Because you're not just saying, 'Where is my human culture? Who are my people?', arguing about all that endless identity stuff that everybody kills each other about all day. You're saying, 'I don't even necessarily need to be from the place I'm in, but I can pay attention', to what Aldo Leopold called the biotic community of the place you're in.

So I don't come from where I live at the moment, but as a family we have managed to find a couple of acres to put down roots in and paid lots of attention to everything that lives there. And the community is not just the people.

As you say, you put your feet down in a place, and then you look around and you see what lives here and find out what it needs. You can do that anywhere. It seems to me that if there's an imperative for writers, it is to ask: 'What does it mean to be human, in a landscape, at this time? And what can you do to serve the wider community of everything that lives in it?'

CDC And that's a task as well.

PK There's always an enormous pulling inside you as a writer. In a pre-modern culture, creators would create as part of a tradition bigger than themselves. So a storyteller will tell a story that's part of their culture; or if you're a religious teacher, you've got a big tradition that you're working in. We're people with no tradition, because that's what modernity has done. It's made us all into little individuals. So the story we tell, we have to come up with ourselves. And then we're endlessly in pain, because we're always driven to try and work everything out. Because we're not supported by ancestry, we're not supported by a culture. The bargain of modernity is we have no tradition to hold us back, but we also have no tradition to support us. So all the storytellers have to come up with their own vision which is why writers end up shooting themselves, or drinking themselves to death…

CDC Or rediscovering old myths, old texts…

PK Yes. And what Dark Mountain ended up doing quite a lot of: talking about myths, folk tales and religious stories. Almost unconsciously, Dark Mountain ended up as a place where you could start looking for old stories. One of the things we got wrong in the manifesto was this notion that we need a new story, when we needed to rediscover the old ones. Martin Shaw was one of the people who really made me focus on that, because he said, 'Look, the stories are already here, it's just that we don't know them anymore.'

CDC There's something else contained in these old stories which no new narrative would probably say, which is that you have to go through a process of transformation or on an underworld journey in order to be properly human. So where do you feel that those stories have a place now?

PK The underworld journey and the alchemical transformation is the story at the heart of every religion I've ever come across. An individual has to be broken open in some way, has to go through the fire and come out the other side. That's what our culture is doing at the moment. And all of the official stories that we tell ourselves don't involve undergoing the underworld journey. The green narrative that we can fix everything and it will be alright, is now actually giving way to a more traditional structure in which we all have to go through the fire, and then we'll come out completely transformed into something else.

But we don't like that as a culture. We don't like transformation.

CDC It hurts and you end up in a state of crisis.

PK And you have to go through that… The other thing that religions teach is that you get wisdom through suffering. It isn't popular but life is suffering and how you manage it and what you learn from it must be the lesson of life. We have created a culture which tells us that progress will prevent us from suffering. We like that story because no-one wants to suffer but it's not working, it's just delayed lots of suffering that we're going to have to go through now.

So the heart of the story that interests me now is what it means to go to the Underworld and come back marked, but with some wisdom. You know, Odin has to be hung on the tree for nine nights, and then he has to lose his eye, before he gets the vision that's given to him in the runes.

CDC There's a story cited by Derrida via Plato about the invention of writing. Thoth, the Egyptian god of medicine and magic, tells the king he has created a method that will help the people remember and be wise. But the king tells him: the people will put all their wisdom in the writing and forget to hold it themselves. Eventually he agrees, with the warning that henceforth writing will be both a poison and a remedy. He calls it the *pharmakon*.

It seems to me that writers often embody the medicine of the pharmakon themselves and that your journey as a writer, and in *Savage Gods* in particular, relates to the holding of these contradictory forces.

PK Yes, the question at the heart of that book is: how much in these words is so divorced from the thing they're pointing at that they are useless or damaging?

In the book I talk about being torn between this notion of sitting around a campfire with my tribe and wanting to be part of that long lineage tradition. And then wanting to sit up on the mountain and look down at the campfire and go, 'Look at all those idiots just being comfortable around their fire instead of coming out here and exploring what might be possible.'

That's the human condition. We're all around the campfire and on the mountain. As a writer, you're never going to be content with either. And that's OK, so long as you can hold that as your work.

I'm very content in my personal life. But existentially and culturally and ecologically, no. If you do the kind of writing that happens in Dark Mountain, if you don't think the world is going in the right direction, or the culture has got it right, or the stuff that surrounds us is the stuff that we should be surrounded by, you have to carry that contradiction all the time. And I'm better at carrying contradictions now than I was ten years ago. You just have to carry it and not be eaten by it.

CDC The writer, within the frame of the story, is also a rememberer of a certain kind of wisdom, whether it's remembering how to be with the land or remembering the old stories, bringing them back into the field of attention or acting as a bridge to the non-human world.

PK That's the big story for me now. How can you possibly tell the story of the world that isn't human? How do you build a culture which sees the world as a living, sacred community of which you are part? Because you can either do that, or burn. And out of the ashes of this whole machine will have to come a re-attending.

CDC And do you think words are part of that?

PK I had a conversation with the writer Charles Foster recently at the launch of *Savage Gods,* and the conclusion we both came to is that if words have a value that's the value they have. Can words come out of a bigger tradition that carries them, that is not just about you as a person, torn between your various desires, but as part of a grand, living tradition?

What happens if you go to a place and try and write it? In a way that carries the stories of that place, that sees that place as a living, functional network that's watching you at the same time as you watch it. How would you write if you were trying to write that? And the answer is: entirely differently. And I don't know whether you can do it in prose.

CDC A lot of poets get close to it.

PK I wonder if it's still something that poetry does that prose almost can't do. I did an event in New York in 2017 with Amitav Ghosh, who wrote *The Great Derangement*. And we had a conversation about what would it look like if you were trying to write the non-human world. And he said in some of the old Indian stories it's totally natural to have the land speaking. It's true of the old fairy tales of Europe as well: you get speaking trees, you get magical things happening in woods. And it's all completely standard. It's just assumed that if you go into the forest, everything's alive and weird things are going to happen. So, it's not magical realism, it's just realism.

CDC One of the things that's so difficult is that the planet doesn't speak rationally, so you have to learn another language.

PK I think it probably doesn't speak in modern English prose, if it speaks any human language. It certainly doesn't speak in the kind of literary prose that I thought I had to write. The act of paying attention somehow creates a different kind of writing – analytically, intellectually. It's all experiential.

Most humans throughout history have not spoken or communicated in literary, analytical prose with each other. Or rational, modern conceptual language… Every language is obviously very particular, and we're talking a slightly bleached version of English that's become the language of the global machine. You talk to Irish people, and they say that the words that you would use to represent a certain feeling or a sense of place or time, are very different from those the English came and imposed upon the people.

And that's why empires, including the British Empire, want to wipe out indigenous languages: you people speak English, because that's the rational, modern language of industry, the language of the civilised people. You get rid of all of the words that allow you to relate to your places and your culture and your ancestors, because that's the way we destroy a people. We take their language away.

CDC So how do we decolonise, to use a very modern term, our own words?

PK For those of us who are English, or who speak English, it's almost a harder task, because, you know, if you're Irish you can at least relearn your original language, whereas what's our original language?

CDC In some ways with *The Wake* you went back to something like this…

PK Well, one of the things I was trying to do was to explore one version of the original language of the people of that place. Regional languages might be another answer, all the dialects that have been wiped out all across England, by this southeast BBC English that I was brought up to think was the way you were supposed to speak if you wanted to get on.

CDC But when we are stuck in this imperial language, we also fail to see that other, particularly indigenous, people outside Europe have a different way of looking at reality.

PK Absolutely. Because that's what language is. It's a way of looking at reality. So if everybody speaks the same language, they all look at reality in the same way. That's the purpose of it, that's why it's an imperial language. You eliminate all of those different ways of seeing and relating and you say everyone should speak this one, which happens to be the language of mechanism and progress and machine-thinking and individuality…

It's very Orwellian: if you can create a language which you can impose upon people, it will be literally impossible for them to think incorrect thoughts because the words aren't there. That's the theory behind newspeak.

The minute there's an orthodoxy of language and an orthodoxy of thought, which we all feel we have to stay within otherwise we're going to get punished, or cancelled, then that's the end of expression, that's the end of any attempt to explore outside the boundaries. It's what every orthodoxy from fascism to communism to theocracy tries to impose on the people to purify the culture, by forcing out anyone who thinks or speaks incorrectly.

CDC You've just completed the final book of the trilogy, and then you're going to take some time off…

PK Until the end of the year, I'm not writing anything, not one word. I've just written this novel set a thousand years in the future called *Alexandria*…

CDC After the library?

PK Yes. At least partly… the great repository of all human knowledge. And the project of that book, at least part of which is also written in another language, is exactly this question of what does language look like when it comes from a non-human place, and how does the Earth speak when it's sentient? So it is ambitious and possibly insane, and disastrous, but it was fun to write and to push yourself forward a thousand years to what the world could be like…

CDC There still is a world?

PK There's still a world. I was really taken with that question about landscape that speaks, sentient landscape, how people have relationships with and communicate with things that aren't human, that's really central to the book. The narrative of the human body and how it relates to the body of the Earth.

If you were looking to the next ten years of Dark Mountain I would say that's the big question. If the Earth doesn't speak in prose, what does it speak in? How can you hear it? And how can you possibly represent it in words. How do you get this burden of machine English off your shoulders and start to plunge into something messier? Almost like taking the language back a thousand years, or forward a thousand years…

CDC Which is what you've done…

PK So, if you want to see things differently, you have to have different words to see them through, or different words to express. This language, as it's currently spoken, certainly written in prose, is not remotely adequate to represent what you can actually see and feel when you go into a forest – it's the opposite of indigeneity.

CDC The roots must be there though. Orwell advised writers to use Anglo-Saxon words, and avoid the abstract Roman or Greek ones, because they are based on things that you can touch.

PK They have to be there, yes. All the languages must have been earthy and indigenous and rooted once. This culture was just as indigenous and rooted as any other one before it became modern. So the question is: how do you get through to it, how do you get through to the root of things?

[overleaf]

MAT OSMOND

Listen (excerpt from *Deadman & Hare*)

Ink and mixed media on paper

Hare feels her nostrils flare, her mouth
water. There's something she can't see,
tugging on the page. Hare shuts her eyes
and listens, and there it is. Eating.

Deadman & Hare: two characters locked in a perpetual comedy of errors; a broken miracle play stuck on a loop in which Deadman seeks to pull away from life, and Hare quietly, relentlessly thwarts his efforts. From an ongoing series of illustrated poetry pamphlets about the mindset of ecocide and what heals it.

Sarah Rea

An Owl, Cleaved from its Wings and Claws

I've travelled as far as Odysseus from Ithaca since the time I first heard tell of a gathering in the night woods. Since I sat, back to a knotty pine wall, typing my first honest words in an epoch.

Since I gingerly set them aloft. I still write this way, back against wood, legs outstretched. Wetting the tip of my index finger and smoothing my eyebrows, feeling for grit between my incisors. One bottom tooth is sharp to the touch from the infinite times I've dragged it under my fingernail bed, looking for the right words.

And the dog still lies, washed by snow on a white duvet, instead of brown and flea-bitten in the back of my truck. His eyes are milkier, his gums bloodier and his joints flex gently as he chases down flying things in his dreams.

I only live across town from that time. I can smell the fires from Ithaca's shore.

But I've been joined and unjoined since. Declared myself whole to the wide world and been unceremoniously disassembled in an operating theatre. I've lifted a jug of whisky to my lips before the house awoke and spent the day curled around my own knees. Risen before the sun to demand the pistons in my chest do something, anything, but quiver like a kicked mongrel.

There was a time that the colours disappeared completely.

Before, I was a baker, a travelling minstrel. I ate fried dough in a swamp in Louisiana and watched men in colourful tatters chase chickens in the freezing rain. Ate a sow's belly from a smouldering cauldron. I watched plastic door handles snap in the snow and I left the windshield-struck body of an owl, cleaved from its wings and claws, on a promontory in the Appalachians.

The music in my head woke me up when I was sleeping.

I have a retirement plan now. I discuss compounding interest. My belly is barren and I'm afraid to fill it. Afraid it might not take to filling. I keep a green notebook full of little squares that are checked when I change my engine oil or send some small token to a child not bound to me by blood.

Some mornings when I wake, there's a tang that's sour and old, and I shoo it out with incandescent pine and black tea and maple.

And some mornings, the birds streak across the blue and give way to clouds, and the hoarfrost-hung air gives up no smell at all.

And it's easier to soothe a dull ache with skittering blue light than to pull a knife from its sheath and tease out slivers from a red-run hand.

I first wrote to share the story of a fire with a covey of kindred spirits, and then again when I pulled things from the earth and felt they bore repeating. And I've been grateful this world has kept me haunted.

It is a gift to know there are others that sit with pottery shards spilling through their fingers, listening with curiosity to the sound of clay hitting stone.

Jay Griffiths

Coral

Have I ever misread something so terribly?

I thought it was beauty.

Recently, snorkelling in shallow waters in Indonesia, I saw some pieces of coral glowing electric blue, a colour so strong it filled the waters with a fluorescent melody, a ringing blue that sung itself out – out – to the realm of ultramarine. I had swum across swathes of dead coral that day and was shocked and saddened. This blue coral at least seemed vibrantly alive and possessed of an utterly ethereal beauty.

Over a decade ago, I trained as a diver so that I could write about coral reefs in my book (*Wild: An Elemental Journey*) but in no dive back then had I seen coral of this pulsing glow, lit from within, luminous as a bluebell wood at twilight.

What stays in my mind from a decade ago are the colours of a coral reef. Here small fish, anthias, play a yellow scherzo, there the orange of an anemone fish shines out. The blue and yellow of the surgeonfish is like laughter across the reef and the parrotfish gleams like a paradise of gold and turquoise. The fire dartfish zooms into view, its body all the colours of flame from its pale yellow head to tawny embers at its tail.

Coral, the living part of which is made up of tiny creatures called polyps, is an underwater shapeshifter. It looks like ferns and reindeer horns, like frosted trees and feathery fireworks, like fans of gold and white lattices; while whip coral looks like an ancient anchor, ropes of coral look like necklaces made of moss crushed with diamonds, sapphire and shells. The coral reefs I saw ten years ago made me think of culture as well as nature, renditions of civilisations: the patterning of Islamic art, a hint of Borobudur, a quote from the pyramids, or pointillisme or modernist pottery, they create their ornate architecture in trellised balconies and stupas.

Nothing expresses vitality like a coral reef. Angelfish look like they invented iridescence, their fins trailing the glory of it. In vivid proliferation, in this world of reckless beauty, life is lived only in rainbows. For thousands of years, the coral world has existed mostly unseen by humans, in a phantasmagoria of psychedelic dreaming. It is now spiny, now prickly: coral may be fiddle-headed or pronged, spirally, whorled, tubular, gauzy or gossamery. It appears inexhaustible in its profusion, a kaleidoscope, a wonder, laughing with sunlight, swaying and thriving in the sheer *ivresse* of life.

Coral reefs are as necessary as they are beautiful. Fish come here to spawn, as the reef offers protection for eggs. Sea mammals including dugongs raise their young on the reefs. Various medicines, including prostaglandin, come from coral reefs. Reefs are home to a third of the species of the sea and are entire communities of inter-thriving life. Coral acts symbiotically with algae which live in coral tissue, and the algae photosynthesise, turning sunlight into food for the coral.

In the summer of 2015, more than two billion corals lived in the Great Barrier Reef. Half have now been killed, largely due to the crisis of climate change and the overheating of the oceans. 93% of the Great Barrier Reef suffers some level of bleaching. 29% of it died in 2016. A 2017 UNESCO report found that bleaching had impacted 72% of World Heritage listed reefs. Based on current trends, bleaching will kill most of the world's coral within 30 years and, because it is a fundamental part of the ecosystem, the death of coral will cause a terrible collapse in the wider life of the oceans.

When the oceans become too hot, the coral expels its algae and the result is first bleaching, then death. Without algae, the coral starves. Further, nothing thrives around a famished reef. In the endless expanse of deadness, on that ghost-reef recently, the only fish I could see were grey, eerily translucent, camouflaged in this colourless coral, hanging listless in the deadening waters. All the colourful reef fish I saw a decade ago – the fish like wishes in their brilliant and shimmery shoals, their gold and purple swift as psychedelic electricity – can no longer find camouflage in the ashen coral and have fled.

When coral bleaches, it can go white in a couple of weeks, as if enacting a poignant image of grief and shock. Of this coral are bones made. Broken. Lifeless. Skeletons. The endless grey of pallid, lifeless ashes, sunk into dust. This is what I was looking at, when suddenly, in the midst of the devastation, I saw that unforgettable luminous blue, fluorescing and electric. I thought I was looking at beauty. I wasn't. When I got home and researched it, I found that I had been looking, unknowingly, at death foretold. Not looking at beauty but at tragedy played in blue.

When coral gets too hot, it produces a chemical to try to protect itself from the heat, and this is what makes them luminesce in this unearthly way for a mysterious moment. They still live but will die, and in this moment between, they shine. It is the coral's swan song. Richard Vevers, creator of the film *Chasing Coral* describes it as 'the most beautiful transformation in nature. The incredibly beautiful phase of – death. It feels as if the corals are saying *Look at me. Please notice*. This is one of the rarest events of nature happening and everyone's just oblivious to it.'

When you dive deeply, colours disappear. As you first dip underwater, skeins of fluent light surround you, but diving deeper the light fades and colours disappear one by one. The rays of reds are gone by 200 or 300 feet. The rainbow is inexorably reduced. After the yellows and greens give out, only blues and violets remain. Then these in turn give way to ultraviolet, the colour we cannot see. The ultraviolet reaches deepest of all, beyond our sight, as the prefix 'ultra' means beyond.

Ultramarine means beyond the sea, and watching this blue coral glow in its moment between life and death, the ultramarine has a timbre all its own in the deepening. Blue is the colour of both grief and love. Blue fathoms the past and is the colour of eternity. Gazing at this coral, in the indigo, lustrous and low, what I was seeing was the time between its life and its death, the blue hour, the last colour you see before the abyssal depth, an ultramarine sung in the key of dusk, radiant into a world that ignores it, and sinking, ultimately, into invisible and anguishing ultraviolet, an ultra-dying at an ultra-twilight.

Jane Lovell

Shearwater

listen
this poem has been dredged
from deep in my belly

there are words spilling out
that will last for centuries

beak pulled wide
            here stares
the curdled tongue
of a starling, of a lark
of a million birds airborne
and silent
                        no song

just this convulsive, compulsive
spew of shards and scraps
the twisted film
of something foreign

fragment   shard   sharp   slip   swill

skin snipped open
muscle drawn
gut exposed, stretched white
packed tight
erupts

like half-sucked sweets:
beads and bottle caps, biros,
lighters, pen tops, applicators

look up: sea lap
a tide thick with curved print

we did this

there are words in it
that will last for centuries
that will survive us:

Polymethyl methacrylate
Polycarbonate
Polyethylene
Polypropylene
Polyethylene terephthalate
Polyvinyl chloride

planet

Harvye Hodja

The Shadow Protagonist

The land is covered with trash and shines with blinding light. Trees lust for sky, die of knots. You can't drink the water, stagnant. People flow downhill to liquification. Weather blows up from town, discharges sulphur and meat, rains ash, and there's an avalanche of bloated guts rumbling down the sweltering spring slopes. Butterflies nest on faeces, death caps grow, and the sky, blithering with dirt, haemorrhages colours you could scoop out with an iron spoon. Eternal, mighty, implacable.

Lo;

Is it better to be hopeful? Undoubtedly. Is there any point in being hopeless? No. I suppose psychologically it is difficult *not* to re-assert hope, to respond to the awfulness of the all-around by throwing up a last defence. Living in hope is a better way to approach tragedy than almost any other, especially when that hope is tempered by being steeped in the realities of despair, death and annihilation. I applaud hope, and wish I had the courage and, frankly, work ethic to live in its lifeboats. But an undercurrent pours into the void and I am sinking in front of the iceberg as you row gamely away. I am mesmerised by the eerie curves of the ice under the ink. It is unbearably beautiful. By god, it is a holy thing.

*

My decade started late. In the spring of 2011 the edge of the Earth was peeled back and 20,000 people were killed in a few minutes on the Japanese coast. I was not far away, further south and watched the skyscrapers sway against each other in relief against the still blue behind. Within a few days I was in the heart of the disaster area as part of a relief effort. There, the air, water and land had briefly merged. Somewhere nearby, nucleics danced in the winds and submerged everything into chaos, impregnating us with radiation, real and imagined. It was a tiny thing, the tsunami, on an Earth scale – an immeasurably small portion of the sea's water. Yet, those dead, so many to us.

God does not care about us and has no interest in us. We are fragile and erasable. We built on that coastline and were wiped out, as if we had not existed. Months later one of the survivors, an older woman living in a tiny temporary shelter, told a newspaper: 'Even the clouds are different'. Some things end and cannot be put right. God is a brutal killer and does not know what it is doing. It just does.

We scoured the town for the living; the town was full of the smell of the dead. The smell literally stuck to us – stuck to my boots all day long, because it was in the mud. We visited a school gymnasium where bodies were laid out by the hundreds under blue tarp; my hands shook so badly I couldn't hold a pencil. And the smell was always with us. From this? From the many unfound bodies in yards all across town? Or from the fresh ocean mud, full of millions of freshly dead other things, tiny, unknowable, uncared for?

Did it matter?

We worked 20-hour days for eight days before they decided we'd had enough. I remember a man working with a shovel by his mud-covered house in his mud-covered neighbourhood. Shovelling up ages of mud, one scoop at a time. This is how we whom god forgot recover.

In the unravelling of that town, I spent eight of the worst days of my life and, if I am honest, some of the best. Darkness rose up and consumed the coast. Coated life, extinguished it, left nothing the same, slathered the land in uncharted misery. Changed the clouds – a bereavement in totality.

Yet everything was shot through with hope, and light, rent and broken but palpable. The man with the shovel. As we unravel, one great mystery of the darkness is its horrible beauty.

*

Sitting comfortably in a warm house one Wisconsin winter, I took an online quiz about what-religion-are-you, slotting myself into myth. Who am I, computer? I asked. I thought I would be a secular humanist: as a child I was raised in the refuge of that worried intellectual, Unitarian Universalism, and as an adult I attend no church.

I made my way merrily through the quiz: a time-numbing interaction with my digital overseer.

The outcome, totally unexpected, disoriented me: my computer said I was a neo-pagan. A *what*?

I hadn't heard of that. I imagined something too committed, too silly, for what I wanted to be.

Reflection sometimes brings me to my senses. Who knows what goes on in the guts of the algorithm but based on the questions it asked I am guessing the computer assigned me to neo-paganism on two axes: first, belief in god with a small g. God that is everywhere, always, and is all things: good, bad, and mundane. A god equally manifest in sidewalk cracks, brightly painted orange cardboard laundry detergent containers and twerking. Each tiniest abomination and blessing. Existence our single miracle: not that we are here, but that anything is here at all.

Second, because I assign no positive moral value to god. If god is everything, god is love. Yes. But god is also evil. God loves evil just as much as god loves love: god gets wrapped up tight in bad junctures and flows out, vile and cruel, sometimes in great killing gouts. Even while spattering us with light and mercy, god rains horror on us too: octillions of bits of masticated birdshit, scattered in ten thousand tornados of chaos. I don't like god's bunching and mulching of foulness and hate, and I won't worship that part, but it is inseparable from the never-ending true-ness of the all. Everything is eating something else.

We are being churned back into the dark – we are dying, every moment, all the time. Yet, we pierce through the solipsism of that: recognise that our frame of reference, the *all* here on our ball of gas-shrouded dirt, is dying too, going to blind dust perhaps somewhere closer to now than eternity. With insects, plants, animals, air, water, colour, freshness, vitality, age, richness, truth and pleasure: a horrid, careless, blind shuddering and shattering.

In response god shouts – nothing. The night mountain avalanches rotten ice and snow. We shear into the ground, desiccated, preserved or putrid, and the rain continues unabated, mashed up together with life.

*

'Whither goest thou America, in your shiny car in the night?' Jack Kerouac once asked. *Right here* seems to be the answer: nowhere and everywhere, all at once. Not just America: we are all going – somewhere, nowhere – in our shiny car, through darkness.

The presence of the infinite, pressing on us, a moment away, ready to take back the liquid sack of our body. In our shining car in the night we seek oil, meat, heat, light, and every good thing we've ever wandered up the wrong valley looking for. We test limits in the wasteland, check if ecstasy is on offer, death, the time when all things become no-things and we ascend into them. *It… is… right… there!*, we think. We think we have but to reach out and take it. We seek the kernel until it hurts. Singe our wings, swallow the smoke, get consumed.

We are wax, our evaporation so slow as to be invisible to the naked eye – until the wick gutters out.

The obsidian mountain gleams, blares out our eyes. We are smouldering, touching the light, incandescent.

*

Nobody wants to give anything up.

Sometimes this is a simple thing.

Simplistically, one day during graduate school in our cushy university town, I told Jed his SUV was an embarrassment and a kind of sin. He said yes, but that he likes feeling safe.

Selfishly, a different year, walking up a valley in Nepal strung with a jarring, ugly, unending line of power wire, I said it was an eyesore, and that I didn't want electricity in this place. Fine, you try that on a dollar a day, said my friend.

Much later, in the disillusioned years of first jobs, visiting Vince and Sarah's cob house in the American South, built with their hands from the river bed, taken wholly off the grid, we wanted to dry our hair. We'd brought our hair dryer. Vince and Sarah said yeah, go ahead, we'll turn some lights off, so there is enough power. We said fine. No problem. No problem: when Vince, Sarah and I convince a hundred millions to turn off the lights to dry their hair, or better yet use a towel, we will have won. Which is why we have lost. A few hundred million may smile kindly at us, then leave the lights on while they dry their hair. Because that is what they want. As I tear my daily carnage through the planet's vanishing skin, I eat the same end.

Sometimes it is a more complex thing.

Numb tourist, having trundled over these years through Dachau, Hiroshima, James Island, and a dozen other horrors, in 2001 I landed in Cambodia on vacation and dutifully attended their apocalypse, between stints at Angkor Wat and the beach. At Tuol Sleng, prison torture centre, my empathy-deaf analyst crept out. I knew it was all true but complained to my friend that they had damaged their own narrative: among the thousands of photographs of the dead were many that were clearly repeats. This felt careless and dishonest and helped my analyst build my shield. Next, at the museum at the killing fields, my inner analyst rejected the map of the country made of human skulls, because who but a macabre teenager or outside conqueror would build such a thing? It reeked of the continuation of killing, not its end. My process of self-distancing.

Then I dragged my cynical carcass out to the actual fields, where they say they severed neck cords with pick axes to save bullets. Resentful of the crassness of my deed but thirsty, I bought a Sprite from the man selling them out of an ice-cube-filled cart, so I could avoid dehydration. Commercialism: endless winning.

I leafed through my guidebook for curated mass-market meaning, but the drink seller kept trying to tell me things. He swore a lot, referring repeatedly to the 'fucking Khmer Rouge'. He told me the bits of white things in the ground around were human teeth, saying 'bastard' and 'shit'. Trying to convince me? To suppress? To deal with it? I don't know. In his reactivity, the truth bloomed all over us, covered us and the dead with pheromonal rivers of hate, fear, guilt and confusion. And he got 25 cents for a Sprite. To make a life.

*

Lo;

When I get out of this city in my gas burner, drive up into the hills of New York or Pennsylvania, at first I rejoice. I had forgotten how much green, how many heaving hillsides of trees, how many miles and miles uncluttered, unclaimed, untaken, unused. For an hour or so of this, I feel I've been ridiculous: things are just fine. Silly me and my darkness.

Hope, the shadow protagonist, garlanded with beauty, stretches back across memory.

Moss agates sproul and grow. Salt air lathers bamboo grass; bear pelts drag through ticks, burrs and yellowed paper fronds. Drops rain, and ooze grows and congeals on slickrock; starlet leaves spook the daynight. Dust in meltwater, line of ashen bluff above green mere, mosquito clad, dewed with time and forgotten. Larch of algae along scree, stir of silt around birdleg. Pulsating coagulation of sea, nestle rock and fern. Flower-shodden cliff, black tree boles strike the sky. Craze of autumn hue clambers the scarp, faces gravel flats, S-bends: ebony swamp mud, lime sky, susurration of birds in kilted air. Tundra collects dung, bacteria and clouds. Cirrus removal.

Yet everywhere, sharp darkness devours us.

In Gao, Mali, on vacation again, see how they disembowel the cats, throw them over the wires. See how we send the goats and cows to eat in the dump; packed dirt and plastic shards. Near Chicago, in my shiny car crossing and re-crossing America, out the window rivulets of caked rust. Earth scraped out. Smokestack spires, industry saints. Dirty grass speckled with tar, potash and mercury. In Suriname, driving down to admire the jungle, find instead firehose gold hill, aluminium strangle. Sugar, cotton and cane to broken glass, grace blown out, scraped, corroded, mildewed, unusable, no salvage or safety. In every country: fences, holes, soot and neverending windblown tyranny of styrofoam bits. Fish in the Sahel mudhole, along the Japanese concrete canal, or on the blaithy American river, blooming with the stink of what you can't find. At the wet edge of the Serengeti, seeking lions, sleep blanketless in the jeep tracks that go to every last place; lie in the impressed mud of the tire tread, human familiarity in the sodden taken-scape. Crossing Arizona on my bicycle, I slowly pass mile upon mile of close-penned beeflings awaiting slaughter under the silver sky, next to flattened arsenic dirt. Denude the flank of the Earth, kill each plant we need, strew the empty places with sheets of corrugated zinc. Burn every last thing. In Kathmandu, out for a stroll, watch my neighbours wash dishes in the foetid stream; over the years the press of the city has scraped the riverbank bare, clotted the braids of the water. Outside town we cover the calf corpse with flaming chaff, shear away the head, singe off our hair, eat our flesh for nothing. Bones and guts fragrant in grey chemical snow. Trading for what we want, we get what we don't: smoke for clouds, coal piles for water. Septic fiberglass slivers our skin as we brush along our lives. Savage desolate passion, decay, and balm.

If the rise of darkness and leaching of beauty is one emotional extreme and these snow-dusted vacant fell-tops another, as hours on the road pass by, a median reality creeps in, obliterates extremes, seeps into my eyes, pores, nostrils and withering flesh. Beauty, yes. But even in those spots of seeming refuge, the world is tied down: by electrical wires, roads, contrails. Skeins of windblown plastic, shredded and torn, ghostly in the branches.

*

Hope's bell. Dusk. An ecstatic, terrible joy.

John Rember

Things I Think About While Running Uphill

Last summer Julie and I skipped my 50-year high school reunion, even though it occurred within driving distance of our home, at a nice restaurant, on a warm sunny evening. Facebook photos show people smiling and laughing through dinner, most of them still recognisable in spite of compressed spines, wrinkles, walking aids, and tufts of hair missing from scalps and sprouting from ears. I would have liked to talk with some of them, to see if they still recognised the world we had graduated into at 18. I would have liked to see if they still recognised me.

But we stayed home, opened a bottle of red, and ate curried lamb outside on the deck while a sunset flamed and then darkened. I toasted my classmates. Julie toasted them too, and said she was glad I didn't marry any of them. I said if I had been perceptive enough to see them as the beautiful young men and women they had been a half-century ago, I would have married as many as I could.

The past year has seen a number of those beautiful young men and women die. I regret not taking the opportunity to engage with them before cancer or heart disease did.

At some point, the biggest blessings in life become good health, intact cognition, good food and the taste buds to taste it, a sunset and the eyes to see it, a long-lasting love and the unselfconsciousness to feel it. At some further point, the one I'm at now, they become an embarrassment of riches, reason enough not to show up at a late-life reunion.

Our high school was small but that didn't keep its students from creating an elaborate class system based on wealth, team sports, car ownership, and physical and social attractiveness. My family was relatively poor, my social skills non-existent, my sexuality repressed, my intellect larval. I took up the loneliest sport, long-distance running. When I did go out on a date, it was usually because well-meaning friends were trying to get two losers together. At least that's what I thought at the time. I was half right.

Adolescence wasn't kind to me. It would have been a comfort to know that adolescence has never been particularly kind to anyone. But I ignored as irrelevant any evidence that I wasn't alone in my suffering.

Things have changed, after 50 years of occasionally-deliberate self-improvement. I can be at ease in public now, for an evening, or at least for part of one. I've quit dressing funny, mostly. I've memorised jokes, except for the punch lines. My hair is white, though it still covers my head (and sprouts from my ears). I'm no longer alone. Julie is a beautiful, convivial woman who could have found any number of people to marry, but she married me, and our marriage has been a long-term happy occasion, marked by laughter and compassion.

I might have rented a Porsche, invited Julie to occupy the passenger seat, grabbed my tweed jacket and my latest book, and roared off to the reunion, there to erase as much of my high school's class system and social shame as possible.

I couldn't do it. Adolescence isn't safely closeted in my past. At random moments the mirror shows my high-school face instead of a distinguished professorial image. The thing in the mirror smiles a slack-jawed smile and makes a noise halfway between a giggle and a whimper.

It isn't just reunions that bring on adolescent horrors these days. It's the nightly news. It might be tempting for Americans to see Donald Trump as a singularity, an accident that won't happen again, a chance rearrangement of genes by a rogue particle of Alamogordo fallout. But many other nations have leaders or would-be leaders who seem well-marinated in the resentments, lonelinesses, and unsatisfied lusts of a 15-year-old male.

Who comes to mind besides Trump? Leaders of the Phillipines, Poland, Turkey, Hungary, Russia, Italy, right-wing parties in Britain or France, the demented or dead South American dictators – the demented and dead dictators of any continent. Their methods, once they get going, include beating up, imprisoning and killing opponents, starting wars, and pretending to greatness by assuming the postures, and often enough the uniforms, of teenage revenge fantasies.

These are people compensating for the wounds of adolescence in ways only an adolescent could imagine to be effective. As you might expect, those wounds aren't healing, even as efforts to avoid their pain cause immeasurable pain for other people.

Who pays attention to these people? What things lie lurking in the mirrors of the voters who install these people in office? What things in those mirrors refuse to remember how these people have usually ended their days?

Somewhere in the last 50 years I took up writing, which, like long-distance running, is a solitary endeavour. Its solitude and bearable pain are attractive to those of us still nursing adolescent wounds. It offers at least as many compensations for impotent humiliated rage as politics, and usually hurts fewer people.

Writing has allowed me to stand outside of things, half-wishing to get involved but aware that it can be easier to write things down than act them out. It can be easier to conduct rote interviews with people than to engage with them, easier to write dialogue than respond to it, easier to follow editorial requests than to risk acting on intuition or impulse. Writing doesn't demand that you grow up. Not at first.

Still, when you string a couple of sentences together, they begin to resonate, and that resonance creates a third sentence, which creates momentum, and that momentum can force you to think about things that you would have avoided thinking about, had you seen them coming. You get more engaged with the world outside yourself, even when you would have preferred to stay comfortably within the arena of inarticulate self-pity.

In this way writing becomes a long-term recipe for adulthood, which is not what your adolescent self wants at all. Confronted with adulthood, it wishes it had instead gone into politics.

Intuition and impulse become a writer's worrisome spirit guides. Witnessing, once innocuous, becomes a force of nature, an obsession, an unwelcome and dangerous calling.

We live in an era where being a witness is considered secondary to the actions of the headliners who move and shake events. But when you see witnesses murdered for seeing what they have seen, or imprisoned for what they have reported on, or violently tampered with before somebody's trial, you see how disruptive and compelling a simple human gaze can be. Especially when you imagine looking at yourself from a distance.

Here's looking at you, kid.

I still run long distances. I still run alone – but I still run. That's something on these mornings when I'm scanning the obituary columns for the names of classmates and neighbours.

It's on these runs that I witness the world. That doesn't mean I note every tree or sagebrush or rock in the trail. It means I put together what I remember and what I see in the same way I do sentences, to observe what comes out of their joinings. Now and then I experience the rare it-all-adds-up flash.

Some years ago I took a chainsaw and cleared out an old trail in the mountains behind our home. The trail's a little under five miles, and it gains 800 vertical feet in the first mile, runs along a ridge for the next two miles, and then circles down and around to where it started. It takes me two hours of steady one-foot-in-front-of-the-other, punctuated by steep moments of breath- and soul-sucking pain, to get around the loop. It's worth it, mostly. By the end I'm floating, high on endorphins and the knowledge that I've made it home one more time.

The comedown is brutal. I become aware that I'm no longer a runner. I'm a hobbler. My heart stutters and stammers as I head for the couch.

Out on the trail, I was arriving at deep understandings of reunions and mortality, along with solutions to world-ending problems. Post-run, these matters lack heft and urgency. A nap seems more important. More sensitive and engaged witnessing will have to wait for one more session in the Hobble Orbital Observatory.

*

In addition to writing, I spent three decades of my life teaching literature classes. These classes usually contained one or two students from fundamentalist religious backgrounds.

Many of the works on my syllabus dealt with death in ways that ignored religious orthodoxy. I had to be careful what I said to students who thought dinosaurs became extinct because there wasn't room for them on Noah's Ark. I couldn't tell them that characters who expired in the novels they studied were not bound for heaven or hell.

So I usually issued a blanket statement that death might result in resurrection, but never in the work under consideration. And regardless of what happened after anyone's death, literary character or not, the process would engender major changes in their perspectives and values.

It was a statement that let us get down to the business at hand, and I avoided wrecking anyone's childhood faith.

On one of my recent uphill slogs, I realised that the industrial world – like a character in a long, drawn-out British novel of manners – is dying of consumption. Its death will transform the people who have thus far been complacent in the face of widespread extinctions, plastic in our oceans and on our beaches, continent-wide droughts, shrinking ice caps, the finitude of fertile and non-toxic cropland, and the end of economically recoverable oil.

'There might be people around after the end of fossil-fuelled civilisation,' is what I would tell my students now, 'but they're going to have perspectives and values that will seem utterly alien to you.'

I write this on a glorious spring day. I'm about to put on the superhero outfit designed by the still-adolescent parts of my shrinking brain: black spandex tights with reflective chevrons just below the knees, running shoes marked by fluorescent orange arrows, and an oversize blue and white Led Zepplin tie-dyed T-shirt with the band's Icarus logo on the chest. I will start out the door and head for the first hill, about to save humanity from certain doom – or at least one small part of humanity, anyway. Or at least the cardiovascular system of that one small part of humanity. For a few more years, at least. Maybe.

It's no accident, as the world accelerates toward perdition down a slope made slick by coal ash and sewage, that movies based on superhero comic books are becoming popular. Superpowers are required to save the situation. We need someone with the ability to leap tall buildings, someone who has her own invisible jet plane and magic lasso, someone with a secret cave and a restricted-chemicals lab, someone whose index finger can turn the world to ice. We need another someone who can stretch a fist across a room, or turn into a raging insensate monster who crushes evil beneath his unpedicured feet. We need these people to greet each new day with hope, now that we've seen what superpowers the villains have come up with.

The Unfettered Capitalism family, sequestered in its dark tower, has spawned the Extinction Academy and its unsavoury members: Deep Ocean Blowout Man, SuperStorm, Princess Inequality, Senator Turtle, Insect Apocalypse Boy, Oestrogen Analogue Plastic Woman, North Pacific Gyre Guy, Wildland Arsonist, Dead Zone Walker, and everyone's favorite boo-and-hiss cyborg, Gigaton Methane Release.

Siblings are on the way. In fact, there's an unending line of them, gestating in the enslaved wombs of Minnesotan runaways, overseen by brilliant but insane grad-school dropouts who never met a genetic modification they didn't like.

'In relation to the size of the Universe, the space you occupied didn't amount to much.'

That's what I say to my adolescent self, who catches up with me on my latest run, halfway up the first hill. He's far less out of breath than I am. He weighs less, for one thing. He's younger. He has no concept of his limits, including the limits of his pain. He groans and whines and acts like it's unbearable.

'But considering that you were stuck dead centre in a severely limited narrative character's point of view, you can be excused for thinking that you were right in the middle of everything.'

I'm being generous to the person I used to be, which doesn't often happen.

'You'll need to grow out of thinking you're in the middle of anything,' I tell him. 'For both our sakes, make sure you do. Otherwise you'll condemn us to solipsism, where anything external gets papered over with internal labels. Our minds will move in smaller and smaller circles, and we'll end up in what Hannah Arendt calls "the gruesome silence of a completely imaginary world".'

'Who's Hannah Arendt?' asks my adolescent self.

Lately I've been saying I have a better chance of making it to my 60th reunion than the world does. It's a gnomic utterance that assumes my audience will confuse the end of industrial civilisation with the end of the world, and that there will be an afterlife where you get to remain conscious of who you are and what you did.

Safe assumptions. The end of our civilisation will end the world for most of us, just as it ended for most Romans when the aqueducts were destroyed and they had to drink out of the cholera-infested Tiber. And a conscious afterlife is real, if only in the confines of my endorphin-addled skull. I've already planned out what I'm going to say to my former classmates in it.

'We're all here,' I will say into the feedback-afflicted microphone in the Afterlife Convention Centre. The room we've rented is trimmed in too much smoked glass and funhouse-mirror chrome, but nobody ever said hell was a place of good taste and restraint. 'A hundred percent attendance. How did we manage that?'

'Haven't you heard?' someone says. 'Industrial civilisation went down.'

Questions I'd like to ask at my 60th reunion, if I find the courage to go, if our world hasn't ended, if it doesn't only exist as the last imaginary flash of dying brain cells, if any of us can still hear after dancing in front of eight-foot speaker towers at 1970s rock concerts:

Why didn't Hannah Arendt write about the 'gruesome *tinnitus* of a completely imaginary world?'

That's being flippant about deep tragedy, I know, but my generation has made a habit of being flippant about tragedy and its detritus. In that respect, our world has been just as imaginary as the Nazis'.

More to the point:

Who did you want to be? Who did you become?

When the time came for your own children to go to war, did you tell them to go or did you tell them to stay away? Or did you not have children at all, because you thought war would come for them, too?

Which things do you still remember, besides Vietnam and the draft? The assassinations? Nixon and Agnew? The Apollo astronauts, getting ready to go to the moon, grinning into the cameras? The wisdom of elected officials? Do any of those things contain meaning for you any longer?

How well did your parents die? How well will you?

Are you still seeing your adolescent self in the mirror?

Is there consciousness in eternity? Will that be what it takes to realise you aren't alone in your suffering, and never were?

Not the stuff of nostalgic reunion conversations. Better to talk about where the grandchildren are going to college, and if they got athletic scholarships, and if the tutoring for the entrance exams worked. Better to talk about the nearly-new Pontiac GTO you had as a senior, and how much it would be worth if you had kept it and had taken care of it.

Our 60-year high school reunion, should it occur on this mortal plane, in this civilisation, will happen sometime in the summer or fall of 2028. There's a possibility that the surviving members of the class will be honoured at the fall Homecoming Football Game. If so, we will no doubt be overshadowed by the Homecoming King and Queen, and the princes and princesses from the younger classes.

We will all be 78 or older. If any of us are royalty, it will be of the Bronze Age sort that is murdered at fertility festivals in order for the crops to grow and the rain to fall.

In the ten years since our 50-year gathering, we will have seen the eyes of a few more politicians fade and grow opaque as they fall into dementia. Our own thinking will be suspect. Our political allegiances will be to persons irrelevant – the dead or insane or medically retired or jailed.

Our decrepitudes will be more decrepit. We will not appoint a committee to plan our 70-year event. Our behaviour will arc back toward the adolescent. Our memories will be tinged with the roseate light of nostalgia. Our past will be a safer place, if only by comparison to our present.

One arena where we will be considerably wiser is in the matter of tipping points in climate or politics or finance. The nature of tipping points requires that you look back at them – sometimes a long way back at them – before you can figure out the exact moment when they created the world you live in.

The summer of 2028 will see us giving meaning to what we could have given meaning to ten years earlier, had we known what to focus on: disappeared glaciers, unprecedented floods, currency devaluations, market crashes, extinctions, lethal fungal pandemics, brain-injury lawsuits from the children of demented quarterbacks, economic sanctions, social media frenzies, caliphates of one. Also refugee hordes, starving children, AI-engendered unemployment for professionals, judges disgraced by the people who appointed and confirmed them, whole generations declaring parents and grandparents to be irresponsible bunglers.

I hope I'll still be plowing the compacted earth of memory, even if I do unearth the occasional dragon's tooth.

I hope I won't be alone. From what I've seen of 78-year-olds, loneliness is an occupational hazard.

I hope humanity will be consuming fewer resources and less energy and will be producing far less effluent, and I hope that won't be because six or seven billion of us are dead.

I hope I'll still be asking the occasional awkward question. Here are a couple, one of them easy, one of them impossible to answer:

Remember the nearly-new world you had as a senior in high school?

Can you imagine what it would be worth if you had kept it and had taken care of it?

NICK HAYES
Untitled
Pen and ink drawing

Original illustration for an article 'Voices From the Water' by Alice Attlee, written for the online Dark Mountain series, 'Becoming Human'. The story is about a spring encounter with the River Medway and the activist-swimmers who helped shut down the Kingsnorth Power Station.

Anthea Lawson

Hyde Park to Wembley

A journey in activism

It is July 2011, and I am sitting cross-legged on the dusty ground of Hyde Park in London, looking vacantly at cigarette ends and broken plastic cups. I'm not crying, I'm beyond that. Everyone else is singing along. The forest of legs around my small clearing of gloom is performing the awkward sequence of weight-shifts and jerks that British legs do when their owners are having a good time at gigs, so this isn't Jarvis Cocker's fault. I've loved Pulp since I first heard 'Babies' in 1994. I could have claimed to have been at their legendary 1995 Glastonbury gig if I hadn't been falling properly in love for the first time, missing my lift from a friend who was going to get us over the fence. And now here's Jarvis in all his glory, leaping about the stage, being rude about the offshore tax dodgers who've bought the overpriced flats in the One Hyde Park development behind him. Really, I ought to be enjoying myself.

I've been an environmental and human rights campaigner for nearly ten years, and I've just realised that we're all fucked and nothing I am doing will change that. That is why I'm in despair. This civilisation is hitting its ecological limits and will collapse; the work I am doing cannot save it. Everything I can see here announces the truth to which I have just opened my eyes. The relentless commercialism: merchandise, tat and food stalls lining the arena. The plastic rubbish on the ground. The crowd, dressed in the output of abusive supply chains, unbothered by it all. It's a visual summary of everything I can't bear: our growth-hungry economy, the enormity of unacknowledged and unmet human desires that fuel it, its unthinking spewing of devastation.

This was Dark Mountain's fault. Ten weeks earlier, I'd bought the first book. It found me in Ullapool, at the end of a week of camping and walking among the strange and ancient mountains of Sutherland. One of those small bookshops where everything is so beautifully chosen that you want only to set up home and not leave until you've read everything. That not being an option, I walked out with Nan Shepherd's book about the Cairngorms, *The Living Mountain*, and with *Dark Mountain: Issue One*, which burned a hole in my bag until I could open it.

I read Paul Kingsnorth's *Confessions of a Recovering Environmentalist* in the early sunlight at a campsite near the river Lune, on the way home through Cumbria. I read his despair at the environmental movement to which he had given so much energy, his loss of faith in its attempts to fix the system on the system's own terms. 'I withdraw, you see', he said. 'I withdraw from the campaigning and the marching, I withdraw from the arguing and the talked-up necessity and all of the false assumptions. I withdraw from the words. I am leaving. I am going to go out walking.' I woke up twice that morning. Once in reading bliss: warm in my sleeping bag, tent door open to the cool April air, sounds of birdsong, sheep and the tiny gas burner roaring at a kettle of water for tea. And the second, to an appalling knowledge that I'd already possessed, but been unable to look at.

Even if I achieved all of the 'campaign aims' on the carefully constructed 'campaign plan' that my NGO submitted annually to its funders, it would not be enough. We were working on the 'resource curse' – the built-in tendency of the oil, diamond and timber industries to make impoverished countries poorer, more corrupt and more prone to conflict. It meant tweaking the rules of capitalism, making it play more nicely. But we weren't tackling the values that drive industrial growth; we were just trying to keep a lid on the worst effects.

I had felt like I was doing my bit, even helping to 'win' some new laws to control what companies and banks could do. But I was realising that whatever we did, they would continue to exploit people and nature, because they are driven by their only real imperatives: to grow and profit. Our growth society would continue to breach more and more ecological limits; we would collapse. Indeed, there were many places, outside the bubble of those who benefit from globalised capitalism, where people were already facing collapse. The only thing that might be 'enough' would be a paradigmatic shift in our way of relating to the world and each other. My experience of trying to gain support for much lesser change told me how impossible this might be.

This knowledge had been creeping up on me slowly; Dark Mountain was a catalyst. The dark money investigations I'd been doing, and my attempts to change laws, had schooled me in just how deeply vested interests were committed to the status quo, just how abusive to humans and non-humans the status quo was. At weekends, I was emptying my mind by rock climbing, and the time spent on mountains and cliff faces was kindling a transformed relationship with non-human life. A green door was already opening, and I was primed. The shock of a book full of people acknowledging that we are headed for ecological and societal breakdown tipped me over, into no-longer-deniable clarity.

Allowing in the idea of collapse brought desolation. Friends counselled avoidance. There's no point thinking about it, they said. You can't do your own head in, you have to find a way to get on with the work you're doing. Translated: please, stop talking about it; you are doing our heads in. Meanwhile the modus operandi of the campaigning NGOs I was involved in depended – and still does – upon not admitting it. The only way they can raise funds from grantmakers who have to demonstrate impact, or from the public who – we were told – need a positive story, was to keep on with the narrative that there was something we could 'do'. If I hinted at the limitations of what we were doing, one colleague would put it down to 'your Dark Mountain thing' and we'd carry on as before: action as a form of denial. The only place for me to even think about the possibility of not saving the world was in the pages of Dark Mountain. I felt that I was having conversations with these writers, learning new ways to think. I no longer felt I was going mad.

My response was just one reaction, of course. There were writers and readers of that first book who had been grappling with these ideas for years and were delighted to see a flag being raised in search of fellow travellers. There were environmental activists crashing and burning without the help of Dark Mountain; as the Copenhagen summit failed at the end of 2009, or as Climate Camp disbanded in 2011. There were campaigners who had already experienced deep, isolating grief about climate change in the nineties or noughties and, through grief work, had found a way to act again. 'I didn't have much patience with Dark Mountain,' one of them told me. 'There was too much that could be done.'

There were people involved in the burgeoning Transition movement who were still fairly new to the idea of collapse but – immersed in the story that a powerdown was necessary, possible and, done in community, might even be fun – could hear what Dark Mountain was saying without being jolted out of their sense of agency. When she came across Dark Mountain in 2009, Ruth Ben-Tovim, a theatre maker and community artist, was recovering from a car crash that nearly killed her, as well as experimenting with Transition and designing creative projects inspired by the eco-philosopher Joanna Macy. 'Reading that manifesto shook them all together and I arrived on a different shore,' she said. 'I can remember sending it round to loads of people. Something about the print of it, the font of it, the text of it, the call. It felt like it was a call, and it called me.'

In the fragile ecology of places where collapse could be named ten years ago, Dark Mountain wasn't quite the only niche. It was implicit in Transition's response to peak oil and climate change. It was explicit in Joanna Macy's writing and workshops, which offered a way of understanding grief as part of a process that could move, through gratitude and 'seeing with new eyes', to being able to take action again. However, in different ways, there was still lots of 'doing' in these two. In the Venn diagram that could be drawn of these spaces, Dark Mountain was the only one where 'not doing' was so clearly an option. Sometimes, the most radical thing an activist can do, perhaps, is not to act. Not just as a rest, to gather energy before heading back into the fray, but to step away, with no end in sight.

*

Eight years – almost to the day – after I opened that Dark Mountain book, and I am nine miles from Hyde Park, in a cell in Wembley police station in northwest London. The walls are higher than the room is wide, the white tiles are broken at chest height by a single stripe of blue, and a filthy skylight tells me it is daytime. It's uncomfortably chilly. The wipe-clean blue mattress is hard, albeit marginally more comfortable than lying on the tarmac of Waterloo Bridge on a cold night had been. I've barely slept in 24 hours. I pull my hat down over my eyes, turn up the collar of my coat, curl up on my side and try to rest.

I wake to a high, ethereal melody echoing through the thick walls. I was standing outside the custody suite between 2am and 4am waiting to be booked in with two other protesters, and I will later hear that a chap in his sixties from my town was in the same station; it is unlikely to be them. I don't manage to identify the singer when I am released that afternoon, greeted by a welcoming committee with peanut butter sandwiches and flasks of tea; I can't rule out having heard that singing in my head.

I can still hear it, though. The singing from the police cell, and the singing on the bridge. Of those surreal yet sharply drawn hours when I was waiting to spend the night in the road or to be arrested, when I was so tired that time slowed (parents of small children don't go past 10pm), it is the music I remember most. As the lines of police approached those sitting at the front of our group, and the legal observers started to bob about with their notebooks and pens, energy would rise and we would fire up the call-and-response songs, drums banging, a rising tide of support to those who were submitting themselves to custody.

After a dozen arrests, each taking up to five officers as people were lifted out, the vans would head off to distribute prisoners (they call you that as soon as you are in their hands) to police stations around the capital. We'd be back in the quiet, dozing under tarps and sleeping bags, the support teams passing round snack bars and tea, the moon wheeling another few degrees west. It was in one of those lulls that Helen Yeomans and her London One World choir started singing 'We Got All The Love' in angelic a cappella harmony. 'I wrote it years ago on the back of a cigarette packet and it's somehow become a bit of an activists' anthem,' she says. Funnily enough, that's the precise example provided for 'anthem' in the dictionary: 'the song became the *anthem* for hippy activists.' There are, undeniably, a number of hippies to be found on the internet singing Helen's composition. But that night it felt more than a rousing expression of group bonding. The choir carried on singing as the police returned in stronger numbers; as grandmothers were carried out of our circle of light and noise into the night; as I waited, still, for my turn. The voices, as we started to join in, were both ground anchor and celestial transport. They connected me to a bigger-than-self consciousness that understood every reason in the cosmos why I was doing something terrifying, that previously I wouldn't have contemplated.

*

Ten years on from the Dark Mountain manifesto, its subversive naming of the environmentalist's despair is at the core of Extinction Rebellion. Ten years on, the taboo of the myth of civilisation is being broken, up and down the land, as Extinction Rebellion groups gather and plan. I can't get through a local church hall meeting without feeling tears at seeing this secret knowledge openly spoken and shared by my friends, my neighbours and my children's teachers.

My fear and desolation start appearing in public places. First in that church hall. Then on schoolchildren's banners. I see them in the words of the sixth-former I help with a press release so she can keep on top of her 'A' level revision at the same time as coordinating strikes. By April, my innermost thoughts are appearing in quotes from other Extinction Rebellion participants in the *Financial Times*. These are words I was chary of using in an environmental NGO – what could we do? Either throw it all in the air, or get back down to the campaign plan. Next thing I know, I am stepping into the road at the south end of Waterloo Bridge with a banner. We let a lorryload of trees past us onto the bridge, hundreds of people join in... and suddenly we are speaking our fear and grief in police interview statements and on breakfast show sofas.

Sociological theorising about activism speculates about the factors that are required to create a social movement. The psychology of the individual and their likelihood of going against received cultural conditioning; their family background and whether they were raised by rebels or conformists; their understanding of the causes of the problem and the support they might receive in developing their analysis. Other factors concern the availability of a form of action: the presence or not of organisers, people already doing something that makes sense, who help channel unease, anger and grief into action. Finally, there is the judgment that must be made by each individual, as to whether their joining in is likely to make a difference.

Without a possible course of action that makes sense, you can have all the feeling that something is wrong, but nothing seems to be worth doing. Three years after stumbling upon Dark Mountain, I left my senior job at an NGO and walked away from the campaigning I was doing. I could no longer throw all of my energy into a form of activism whose theory of change, in the face of what is coming – in the face of the infernos, droughts and floods that are already here, for some – didn't stack up.

But what I couldn't quite see then was the egotism in my despair. Of course, there was grief for the world, for the global injustice, for the fate of other species, perhaps even our own. But there was also a personal component to my acknowledgement of collapse, and it was this: if my campaigning is not working, is not 'enough', then the problem is that my actions no longer have meaning.

Jem Bendell, whose academic paper on 'Deep Adaptation' has been downloaded hundreds of thousands of times, offers suggestions for 'living beyond collapse-denial', for the campaigner's difficulty in acknowledging they cannot personally save the world. Recognise, he suggests, that resistance to information about catastrophe 'may come from what you have been consciously or subconsciously telling yourself about your own self-worth, purpose and meaning... If you are a mission-driven professional in fields related to the environment or social justice then expect that you may be driven to rebuild a sense of self-worth and that this need of the ego, while natural and potentially useful, could become a frantic distraction.'

I was not only experiencing grief for the world, but also the loss of what had been my meaningful role within it. As the Dark Mountain manifesto said, even when everything else has gone, we will still have our need for survival, and we will still have our need for meaning. Campaigning is a massive great meaning-generator for those who do it, but campaigners' ideas about what is meaningful – what might be 'enough', what might 'work' – are often organised around the possibility of an outcome.

Having to be reasonably sure of the outcome before embarking on a course of action is precisely the kind of instrumental approach that has got us into this mess. Like the need to put our name to what we do, or the saviour mentality, it's a manifestation of our culture. While campaigning tries to change the dominant culture, without very deep reflection campaigning itself emerges unchanged from the dominant paradigm. Activists forget, too easily, Audre Lorde's reminder that the master's tools will not dismantle the master's house.

Spiritually minded activists have always known that you engage in activism without expectation of outcome. You do it because it is the right thing to do, because it is the practice that matters, not the attainment of a goal. I used to be impatient with any campaign that wasn't fixated, laser-like, on a goal that had to be achievable. Now I can see there is a lot of 'me' in such stories, a lot that is about 'my' purpose. It's also the perspective of privilege. Those who are fighting for their lives, and not from a position of comfort because it is the 'right' thing to do, don't have a choice about whether it will 'work'. And they can't collapse into despair at the prospect that it might not.

I don't think I've ever had such clarity about what I was doing as when I sat on Waterloo Bridge and in that police cell. Yet the clarity existed separately from whatever I might feel about Extinction Rebellion's three aims. Do I actually believe we are going to prompt all of the necessary changes to reach net-zero emissions, to halt the accelerating extinction of species, and to do so in a just way that accounts for the unequal responsibility for our current predicament?

At the first local meeting I attended, we were asked to show our agreement with the statement 'It's too late to avoid runaway climate change', by choosing where in the church hall to stand. The end where the chairs get stacked was 'strongly agree', the end by the kitchen hatch and the tea urn was 'strongly disagree'. Nearly a hundred people were there, dozens of whom would later be arrested on Waterloo Bridge, strung out right across that room. A few of us were doing a jig in the middle. Extinction Rebellion provides space for despair, and it also provides space for acting without needing to know if it will work, or if it is too late, or what will become of our actions.

Dark Mountain didn't know what it would become when it launched either. 'It was only some years in that I saw clearly that this project wasn't the place from which to 'do' anything', wrote Dougald Hine in *Issue 14*. 'We're like a jar of kimchi,' Charlotte Du Cann told me. The vegetables get mixed, are left alone, the alchemy of fermentation takes place. Something is created, we don't know exactly what it will taste like. A cultural space does not have an instrumental purpose.

For Dark Mountain, acknowledging the grief and fear of collapse brought liberation from feeling that you have to act. For Extinction Rebellion, a decade later, acknowledging grief and fear is precisely what allows people to act. I'm struck by the paradoxes. That when you fully acknowledge it may already be too late to change things, you can perhaps start to do so. That, liberated from trying to save the world, you are substantially freer to do something that might be useful. That by naming the impossibility of activism and providing a space where it was legitimate to not act, Dark Mountain may have nonetheless contributed to the emergence of a different kind of activism, one that, like the art and writing it has encouraged, flowers from the soil of grief.

'The way I think about it is a kind of morphic resonance perspective,' says Gail Bradbrook, a co-founder of Extinction Rebellion. Morphic resonance is Rupert Sheldrake's contested yet narratively compelling theory that memory is inherent in nature; that once a shape or structure or behaviour has occurred, it is more likely to occur again. 'It's this idea that some bit of the universe has worked out how to do something, then other people can do it,' she says. 'There's something about the depth that Dark Mountain went into, the idea of stopping and saying: this isn't working for us. That incredibly important piece of work had to be done by somebody.'

*

It might seem strange that there was so much dancing and singing on Waterloo Bridge. Or perhaps it's just typical for a bunch of activists. The damn hippies have blocked the road, now they're having a rave. But for some, the song and dance on that bridge was another form of secret knowledge coming into the open. It was a re-emergence of ways of being that have been flattened by the same processes that have led us to the brink of ecological collapse.

'We had a lot of waiting,' recalls Eliza Kenyon, a voice and movement facilitator.

'We needed to be alert in our dialogue with the police, and relaxed enough to sustain our energy to be there. So we dance and we sing, and some of us call that praying. There was a kind of awkwardness in the bodies, then… it's a buzzword, but suddenly, indigeneity is ours. It's our relationship with the River Thames and the land of the South Bank. That land is speaking through our bodies, and in that moment, that's enough. That's life in its fullness. Not in some veneer of harmony, but in a visceral, all-cells alive togetherness that we can't help but long for because it's part of our original instructions. It's about life and death learning how to dance together, without anybody telling us what to do. Without music, song, dance on that bridge, I don't know what it would have been.

'There's a risk of it seeming fluffy. But these things meet deep human needs for body, song, prayer,' says Eliza. 'Something about that experience on the bridge showed us all our power in a way that we don't often get the opportunity to see. Our food is killed for us, our crops are grown for us, our dance is danced for us on a stage, our song is sung for us. We don't have the muscle, psychically or physically, to be truly human.' This feels true to me. With full respect to Jarvis Cocker, I want to sing, as well as be sung to. In this light, acknowledging despair doesn't just bring the agency to act. As near-death experiences tend to do, it brings an ability to live, to fully inhabit our selves. To live, so long as we are here.

Ben Weaver

The Red Birds of My Blood

After Lyla June and David Wiggins

September 2018, Point Abbaye, Michigan –
I overheard the trees talking to themselves.
I listened as the wind slipped between their trunks
and the red birds of my blood
swarmed through watery stars:

remember that grief and magic co-exist
everything you need is already present inside you
the medicine is scattered everywhere
appeal to people's spirits rather than their training
validate their willingness to deviate
create space for the paradoxes to exist
engagement replaces fear
remember both action and inaction have an impact
this work is an honour not a burden
stay with the inquiry of how it can be better
the future does not evolve in the echo chamber
the future lies in engaging with difference
don't act in resistance or duality
but instead cultivate reciprocity
when you address water and plants
as the living beings that we are
we will tell you profound things
your reality is only as vast
as the diversity of the relationships you nurture
don't personify the river, riverfy yourself
restore your courage in the flash of its teeth
name yourself after the land

don't name the land after yourself
a heart the size of a match will burn out like one too
always work in service of imagination
sit close to the fire and keep it true
do not retreat to your private life
the predictable stories are the ones lived in fear
while the stories with no clear endings or beginnings
are lived in witness to love
transaction and reciprocity are not the same
get as close to the darkness as an owl
consider that the answers you seek
are not material, but rather spiritual, thus forever fluid,
to best receive them you must hollow yourself out
so their messages can ring through you
remember that conflict can be the work working
aim for the heart, to affect the mind
so that hands can reach
do not fret, there is more water coming to join the river.

Eric Robertson

Poor Dumb Bastards

It may be that when we no longer know what to do, we have come to our real work and when we no longer know which way to go, we have begun our real journey. The mind that is not baffled is not employed. The impeded stream is the one that sings.
– Wendell Berry

Out beyond ideas of wrongdoing
and rightdoing there is a field.
I'll meet you there.
When the soul lies down in that grass
the world is too full to talk about.
– Rumi

I don't know who to tell, to be honest. I don't even know why I feel compelled to account for any of these events these last several weeks. I'm not a record keeper. I'll scratch out the occasional poem or fragments of science-fiction novels. But mostly, I loiter on porches. I can't stand for long periods of time. I am of minor consequence to the few infirm people I care for. I know a little about most things, a lot about a few things. But at the moment, all I know is that in the pasture across the busy city street from where I live, it appears that my rich lonely neighbour is about to do something horrible.

But then, aren't all rich lonely neighbours about to do something horrible?

Until today, my view of the pasture was unspoiled. Hot teas and knit blankets to watch the morning sun clip the tops of the cottonwood trees, to smell the Russian olive when the first big heat comes. When the children walk with bags of carrots, it makes me happy to see their tired parents smile, relieved to know their all-day absences don't dim a child's love of the soft and curious nibbles from a horse's big lips. The tiny screech owl comes at twilight and sits in the dead honey locust. In winter, the fox digs in the new snow to pull mice families from their homes nestled in the roots. In hot summers, the horses grazing the property nap under the dead limbs once their morning feeding is done. The pasture has always been an aesthetic balm to all my unplanned convalescence.

I need not describe this neighbour in too much detail. You already know the kind of men who cause the most trouble. His car is what you think it is. His pressed shirts are the colour you think they are. He wears fancy bathrobes in the middle of the day. His haircut, how he smells, the comfort of his shoes – you know instinctively who he is, over there, in the patch of wild asparagus, removing his shirt.

For two weeks this has been coming. One incident after another, what feels like the early stages of some great removal. And I'm only too happy to document it.

INCIDENT 1: Kevin

One of the owners of the horses that graze the pasture comes early to mix food for a skinny thoroughbred. She is of a vigorous disposition. Her strides are long and stretched. Built low to the ground and wide with a head half-shaved, half dyed bright pink. Her voice carries like wildfire.

At the back of the pasture, a young woman kneels in pools of water in hand-sewn clothes. She calls to Kevin, a crocodile. Under the curls of her auburn hair, she is red-faced and confused. Behind the swamp grass, the fox peers out from the dark hole of her den.

The girl with pink hair hears the girl first, calling out through the morning mists – the sweats of a spring thaw rising from the flooded back third. She knows voices like that. The sounds of young women who are not content with the small spaces made for them, but not yet ready to build houses on their own. She pulls a clean horse blanket from the shed and wades into the swampy water and tells the red-faced girl that she has found Kevin and he is safe. The sirens come and the girl with pink hair makes a phone call to a friend who finds the girl a bed where the red curls of her hair will be safe from the men who introduced her to Kevin.

The neighbour emerges from his fake Italian villa built on a knoll to the north and begins his interference by vigorously shaking the hands of the medics and police. He looks at his watch and points in several directions. He pulls a small notepad from his robe pocket and clicks a pencil. He tells the officers of the plague of human homeless that these wild city spaces attract. He too seems red-faced and confused.

You see, this is the problem. They spend the night in the park, smoke some new drug, then wander over here to find places to hide and act crazy.

This is what he says to the medics. I read his lips through my field glasses.

Thank you sir, for your input. We have your number, if anything further comes of this we'll let you know.

This I surmise from the open-palmed gestures and the officer's exasperated expression. Everyone leaves, and my neighbour in a robe is left scratching a summary of the events along with his complaints in his crumpled notepad. Dumb bastard.

INCIDENT 2: The professor and the neighbour in a robe fight over sex

Three years ago, a black quarter horse arrived from Elko, Nevada and was released into the front corral. A middle-aged college professor with a red beard like a Norse earl climbed the gate wearing his grandpa's cowboy boots. His Mexican-Polish husband, a skinny man with knocked knees and long hair followed, with his feet flattened from working a decade on concrete floors selling cheap clothes to young rich mothers. The horse wanted nothing to do with them. Their argument over how to introduce themselves to the mare drew out the neighbour in a robe to introduce himself.

The black mare ran the perimeter of the front corral to get as far away from the professor as she could. His boots were three sizes too big and he dripped sweat like a cartoon turkey on a campfire spit. Passers-by gathered. The girl with pink hair laughed and yelled instructions to a grown man she had yet to officially meet. *You're doing this wrong!*

I saw frustration in his middle-age frame. Not sadness exactly, but the beginnings of a falling apart – in his thick waist, maybe, or his heavy breathing. His heartbeat was meant for admiring great works of art and tending vegetable gardens, not trying to befriend a scared animal to fix a troubled relationship.

The horse kicked and reared up and threw her head. He rushed the horse, arms extended holding a new halter. His boot heels stuck in the soft ground. After ten minutes a very real exhaustion set in. He stopped to catch his breath.

'You can't stop. If she wins right now, you'll never have a relationship with that horse.'

'What was your name again?'

'Samantha.'

He picked up his pace with a near angry determination. The mare matched his intensity, nearly leaping the wire fence. Another five minutes and the girl, in her striped tank top and pink hair, got between him and the horse. He bent down and put his hands on his knees and wiped the sweat from his forehead with the backs of his new leather gloves. The girl gently took the halter and leaned into his ear. She whispered instructions. He slowly nodded his head. The change in tactic worked. Sustained, focussed pursuit, but with no anxious agenda. Another ten minutes and the mare finally turned in annoyance to face what frightened her.

'Turn around. Turn around!'

'What? Why do I…'

'Shut up! Turn around!'

Staring at the back of her pursuer, what the horse's instincts had told her was a threat, now said, *that is you*. Three quiet moments passed.

'What do I…'

'Just be quiet.'

The agenda lingered in him.

'Now, slowly reach your hand back and wait.'

He let go a laboured breath and slowly lifted his arm behind him. A still and sibylline air settled between a human mid-life crisis and an ancient animal's will to safety, in what surely must be the world's most mysterious and troubled space. The horse slowly approached. Four of the onlookers gasped with delight.

'Shh, shh.'

The horse took twenty calm, four-legged steps. Each uneven, each paused and cautious. He rubbed the knuckle of his left thumb over the pain above each eye. Twelve steps closer and the professor's husband stood from his camp chair, lifted by his attraction to the softness and vulnerability in strong-willed men. Then, overcoming the prickly imbalance between fight and flight, the mare softly pressed her nose into the back of his hand. The girl with pink hair collapsed to the ground and sobbed.

'I love it when this happens!'

The small crowd cheered. I shuffled back to my porch. Flickers flew between the cottonwoods. The magpies finished the ceilings in their stick apartments, and the black mare, not two days earlier grazing the sparse winter range of black sage and rabbit brush, settled in to graze on the fresh shoots of Kentucky bluegrass.

And there they've been, four years now. Bringing to that island property horses that people are finished with. Feeding them, touching them, being with them when they die. The pack horses that carried cold drinks and comfortable camping gear for city tourists. The racing thoroughbreds stalled in confined spaces their whole lives but for the infrequent and frantic expectations of their wealthy owners. A hospice made to absorb the vexing residue from thousands of years of one animal bearing the manic amblings of creatures misunderstanding what it means to walk on two legs.

This morning, my neighbour pushes through the gate to the front corral where the horses' hooves are being trimmed and warns the married couple and a wide-eyed Mormon farrier about the bum boys that spill into the pasture from the park to fornicate. The Norse Earl informs him of their membership in that group. The neighbour loudly announces that they, then, are the problem and they'll be closely monitored.

There is yelling and pointing. Arms are grabbed. Arms are raised. Arms are slapped away. As he walks back to his empty house, and after he makes an obscene gesture, the neighbour pulls a black tube blinking a blue light from his pocket and vapes a sweet cherry-bubblegum smoke.

Below the bay window of his villa, the fox runs into her den with two newborn baby rats in her mouth. She steps over a plastic yoghurt cup and one child's pink winter boot. Later that night a raccoon fights off the fox for the dumps of fast food thrown from the windows of cars driven by people who are drunk and high.

INCIDENT 3: The rat and the sparrow

He must have given the rodent to his young kids as a forgotten birthday present, telling them that white rats are magic. I always see them leaving his place with balloons and designer shopping bags. But now, the animals are being returned. This plastic jug is the second one in three weeks, thrown onto his lawn from the window of his ex-wife's SUV. I didn't see if the kids were with her or not.

Before sunrise, I see him squeeze through the pasture fence holding the jug. He snags his robe on the bottom layer of barbed wire as he hurries through the patch of wild asparagus. He turns the jug upside down. The occupant stays wedged inside. He holds it up and reaches through the hole cut in the bottom. The rat bites his finger. In anger, he bangs the sides of the jug, shakes it again, then kicks the jug into the field.

Once the neighbour retreats into his house to change robes and think of a pet no adult would dare return, I wade through the wet switch grass and find the plastic container. It's a white Clorox bottle. Inside, I see white whiskers hide behind a dirty dish towel peppered with food pellets, and a small plush toy – a sparrow. The rat is half black and trembling. I turn my left palm up and reach inside. It sniffs the tips of my fingers then backs up into the neck of the jug. The jagged edges of the opening are covered with black electrical tape. Judging from the makeshift construction of its home, the children were left to care for the animal. Kept in a closet or under the bathroom sink.

The girl with pink hair arrives and takes the rat to a rescue. But then, from the back of her truck, she removes two large metal cages, both carrying what she calls feral cats, to hunt the wild muskrats that live along the creek who find buffets in her horse feed. The cats do nothing but sleep in the cages during the hot days and hunt backyard birds at night. One runs away, the other dies from a grisly fox attack.

Two days later, near the asparagus, a hamster in a Manolo Blahnik shoebox.

INCIDENT 4: The easel, the sidewalk and the idle

The neighbour-in-a-robe's art supplies had to cost more than a thousand dollars. The best tubes of paint. The portable wooden easel. Last week, he set up on the sidewalk to catch the warm sunrise on the silky, muscled rump of the black mare. Like the horse in David's painting of *Napoleon Crossing the Alps* that hangs above the white couch in his living room, the horse reminds him of the trip to Paris with his high-collared wife. That twenty seconds in front of the Mona Lisa with a smartphone camera. The crush of people in the gift shop.

'Goddamn, aren't you a beautiful creature?' He's painted her reared up, the tense strips of muscle in her back legs are spring-loaded. Her front legs thrash the air. He adds a fiery sunset and a tri-coloured flag unfurling in the background. A young girl comes to feed her father's lawn clippings to the horses. He offers her hard candy from his hot pocket. She compliments his work, though his horse looks more like Albrecht Dürer's rhinoceros than Napoleon's Arabian stallion.

On this sad opaque morning, the same frantic woman stops her car at the curb outside my window. She runs across the road convinced, once again, that a sleeping horse is dead. She takes pictures and sends them to her animal watch group, who sends them to animal control, who sends an officer out for the third time this month. She remembers from somewhere in her dusty education that horses only sleep standing up.

She waits in pressed slacks and leather loafers. Her hair extensions cover the new wrinkles in her neck and lay like curls of caramel taffy across her smart cashmere sweater. She lets her German car idle while she waits for the officer to show up. The officer asks the same few questions that will garner the same satisfying answers from the horse owners, but the woman's concern grows nonetheless and inflates into a precarious and sustained suspicion of abuse because, to her, it's all death. It's all death!

'That horse hasn't moved for almost 20 minutes.'

'I think she's still napping.'

'I don't know.'

The woman must have the same empty house. Her only child off to an expensive college. Her husband, always away, feeding algorithms into hot circuits to make young men feel more important than they are, while she wanders the streets looking for ways to be helpful.

'You're a painter?' she asks my neighbour.

'I am.'

'I work in watercolour.'

'Yeah? You should come set up shop.'

'I'm sure I'm not as good as you.'

'Oh, I don't know about that.'

They become attracted to each other through their love of art. They'll collaborate on paintings of native women making baskets and weaving wool rugs on giant looms. She'll buy a matching easel and paint children eating ice cream in public parks and pigeons pecking bits of dried bread left by picnics. They'll sketch kids flying kites and sketch other painters sketching cathedrals. They'll laugh at the irony. She'll invite him to her house and they'll drink chilled wine and talk about moving to Spain. They'll kiss in the back seat of his new Japanese car and lose track of time and be late for the opening act of *Les Misérables.* They'll make love in her English garden, hiding from the brown-skinned gardeners. They'll sell everything they have and retire to their two favourite climates. One hot. One cold. They'll pass away on the same day. Her in the morning. Him later that evening.

This is how everyone thinks it goes for people like them. I know better. I've been keeping track. For his last sex act, he'll masturbate into a cup and force a prostitute to drink it mixed with milk and honey.

The horse finally gets up and moves to the back of the pasture. The lady and her smart sweater ignore his painting and quickly cross the street. She gases her idling vehicle and speeds away to meet with a client about keeping her personal Instagram account on brand.

A strong breeze knocks his easel to the ground. He steps on tubes of paint and smears the colours into the sidewalk with the soles of his leather boots. Instead of turning into the wind to cool the sweat on his shiny forehead, he curses and frantically swipes the Siberian elm seeds from his oiled hair.

While he gathers the pieces of his broken easel, in the front corral, through the stand of cottonwoods, two crows land near the piles of white winter horsehair combed from the thick-faced fox-trotter mare.

They nose through the biggest clumps. Squawk. He pinches a mouthful, she hops over to inspect. Squawks. She rejects his clump. He spits it out. They beak other piles, collect the higher-quality hair and dance toward each other. The birds know that horse people use certain tools at certain times of year to scrape off the horse's winter coats. They know they'll leave the hair behind. They know that winter horsehair is durable. They know that it insulates, resists mildew, cushions and is comfortable. The crows toast each other, beaks full of ancient interior design and fly off.

The hole

He began digging the hole last night at sunset on a midsummer evening. Not unlike the ancient holes dug to trap mammoth and woolly bison. Like trenches dug to skewer invading armies, that drained swamps to cultivate lands that would help consummate forced marriages. Trenches that carry plastic tubes full of electric pulses of light, transmitting voices and secret codes.

It's morning. The fox is done stalking muskrat. The crows copulate in their finished nest. The horses chew at the new starts of red clover. The cottonwoods leaf out, the swarms of painted lady butterflies flicker over the stands of milkweed. The mallards attack both their mates and their rivals. Next to his hole the neighbour takes his pants off. I smile at him from across the street behind my binoculars. He's stopped caring who watches. He either thinks he's invisible or is still convinced he's the centre of attention. The recalcitrant Man. The Man of devils.

The professor and his spindly husband will come to groom their beautiful black mare. They'll see my neighbour standing naked next to his hole. Neither partner will be surprised. Sirens will blare and yet another pale-skinned and plain-minded person will be taken away and given pills to treat their neuroses of wealth. What becomes of the hole is hard to say.

No-one in particular

The big question here, though, is who am I? You'll be wondering why I want to keep that from you? It's for your own good. If I'm a person of god, you'll want to send money and leave your family. If I'm an elected official, you'll run into the street and scream obscenities. If I'm a mother, you'll pity me. If I'm working class, you'll ridicule me. If I'm young you'll lecture me. If I'm educated, you'll call me a faggot. If I say I'm the beaten horse that drove Friedrich Nietzsche mad you'll say I'm a useless metaphor and laugh.

Nevertheless, I've watched this pasture for many years, low-sunk into a soggy, 100-year flood plain, surrounded by a growing city. I've seen others like him in the pasture, some naked, some not. Some engaged in sex, others out of their minds. Teens spray-painting black Xs on the buckskin mustang. Others rolling in the dirt and barking sonnets. One would think they're all mad. But they're not. They're bewildered. Moved by the strangeness of acting wild.

I'll always be here, across a busy city road from a pasture where there are still muddy pools with fever-dream crocodiles consuming all mad ideas. I am the withdrawn. I am the laughter at the wake. So now, I'll just point out that in the pocket of his Italian jeans laying in the dirt, is the tool he'll use. I can see the hard outline. What he'll use to perform his final act. He'll look skyward the whole time, never see the universes crawling in the mud by his mouldy toenails. Never taste for salt or mineral in clotted dirt. Never whisper admiration for the monarchs sucking milkweed. He'll always look for the rarest colours and ignore the pedestrian blacks and whites on the Canadian geese, or the magpies. I don't know where to send my thoughts on what I've seen. I don't know who will care, but here's my advice.

Lonely neighbour, level your gaze and find the horizon. Flatten your feet. Look down.

Stop reading that dark sky, those lights are long dead. Stop naming stars, they flashed out years ago. Never mind the nebulae or streaking comets. Stop stitching together constellations. Let them alone, all spirals and infinites. Look down.

Read your feet, your bare toes on red mud. That toad there. A cricket. Read the brilliant green lichen on grey granite slabs. The swan's-neck moss on cedar bark. The forested floor of fern. Count feathers and footprints. Listen for water underground. Turn your palms down and read the backs of your hands.

You see? Sounds silly and naïve. That's why I mostly keep my mouth shut. I've stopped trying to talk to you. I just want you gone. Quick and easy. Without all this useless drama.

But you must hear something that I don't, neighbour, coming up out of your hole. Is it the voice of some *mother of all nations* calling back her children from your fields of forced labour? Is that what you think you hear? Does she call back the men and women knee-deep in foreign mud, bent at the waist, huffing coal dust or dragging bags of cotton? Does she call out to raise the bones up out of the soils of the Carolinas, Georgia, Alabama, from every acre of North and South America?

Your story is ending. Is that what you hear, what vibrates the walls of your meagre dig? It is, isn't it? And you believe she is calling to you, that she cares enough about you to ask for your repentance. Your hole is your grand, arrogant apology. You think you can crawl back into your origins and that somehow her forgiveness will bring you a better death. If she is making such calls for redemption, they are most certainly not meant for you. You only ever listen to your own voice.

You aren't tuned to the frequency that hums when a Jack Russell Terrier knows that a young child is about to have a seizure. When the brain of an Arctic tern images magnetic fields. You are deaf as fire ants farm and harvest fungus and milk aphids and bury their dead, when the North American wood frog freezes solid every winter, goes months without a heartbeat, then thaws in the spring and is called back alive, from some dark, unfathomable dream. The steady ping of these beautiful and baffling transmissions is what you will not hear, you red-faced, absurd, tiny prick of life. You poor dumb bastard, get ready.

Whatever you do, it's gonna hurt like hell.

Robert Leaver

Man Down

Man Down came about when my shovel broke. I was on a windy uninhabited Irish island just a quick dinghy row off the coast. I was dressed in my vintage blue business suit. The suit my father had made for himself back when he was a businessman. The same suit I wore while *Crawling Home* the length of Manhattan. The same suit I'd been wearing as I dug and occupied dozens of holes in the US and Europe for my *Hole Earth* project. The suit is in tatters but it still works.

I made my way to the highest hilltop and I started to dig. Sparks flew from metal clanging against stone and the shovel vibrated violently in my hands every time I struck a blow. I needed a jackhammer. The handle finally snapped in two and I fell back, catching my breath, secretly relieved and wondering what else could be done.

I decided to lay face down in the field and I asked my photographer friend to take a picture of me as a joke. The picture made us laugh. The image was troubling, absurd and evocative. We tried a few more. Who was this discarded man in a suit? A victim of some crime? A comatose predator? It looked like maybe he'd fallen from a jet plane. Business trip gone wrong? Or was he sleeping off a drunk?

The act of being face down in that Irish field or on the rocky beach by the dinghy got me wondering. Face down I could feel the weight of my body on the earth. The bumps and sharp edges jabbed into my ribs. And I could smell the ground up close, the tide and the loam. I could adjust myself slightly, bend a knee, upturn a hand, and the impact of the image shifted dramatically.

Back in New York I started doing *Man Down* all around town: Times Square, Port Authority, Wall Street. This was not about lying there and letting people watch and gather. This was all about speed. I'd point at a spot, photographer Teddy Jefferson would nod and I'd go down, assume a position, release all tension and then pop back up and walk away. This usually took just a second or two. Hit and run. But the feeling of the

photo does not betray this hasty execution. In most of the shots it looks like this man is down, and he's been down for a while and it is not clear if he is going to get up again any time soon.

Over four seasons I did *Man Down* in the woods, in the dunes, on country roads, in meadows, in streams, barber shops, supermarkets, public toilets, abandoned houses, playgrounds, on highways, and in a stone quarry at the foot of a massive earth-shredding machine.

In a way I suppose these are pictures of defeat and surrender. Collapse forms a question mark. It is human nature to search for clues. What happened here?

ROBERT LEAVER

Man Down

Provincetown, Massachusetts, USA (photo: Teddy Jefferson)

Could be somebody. Could be nobody. A wedding ring and a bad haircut. The clues don't add up. If only we had more time, if only he could tell us. He was here. I saw him go down. And then he vanished.

ROBERT LEAVER

Man Down

Gravel quarry, Catskill Mountains, USA (photo: Teddy Jefferson)

BRUCE HOOKE

Looking Back

Composite colour photograph

The man in the suit looks back at himself as he leaves, momentarily stopped in his tracks by thoughts of the inner worlds he buried when he put on the suit and picked up his briefcase. What has he forgotten? What is he leaving behind to keep up with his life in the modern world?

MERYL MCMASTER

Time's Gravity (from the series 'Wanderings')

Archival pigment print on watercolour paper

'Wanderings' is a contemplation of the limitations and possibilities of the self. Tethered as we are to the past and all that makes us who we are, we look around seeking a world of boundless possibilities of who we might become. In these images I walk into this unknown. (Courtesy of The Baldwin Gallery)

DAVID ELLINGSEN
The Spirits Ebb (from the series 'Solastalgia' – see overleaf)
Chromogenic print

DAVID ELLINGSEN

Unknown Entities – Fishing Buoy No. 1

Pigment ink on cotton rag

Using fine wire rigging and long exposures of seconds and minutes in combination with the currents of wind and water, the photograph reflects a reality of plastic, one of the most ubiquitous substances on the planet, as an unknown entity literally diffusing, dissolving and evolving into the fabric of life itself. While common sense might suggest some disturbing conclusions, scientific studies are only just beginning on the long-term health effects of these compounds.

David Ellingsen

Solastalgia

> As opposed to nostalgia – the melancholia or homesickness experienced by individuals when separated from a loved home – solastalgia is the distress that is produced by environmental change impacting on people while they are directly connected to their home environment.[1]

While there are still many days of fresh, vital life here – bracing winds from the wide Pacific, the crisp rains charging energy, the visceral delight in the briefest glimpse of whale, seal, bear or mink – breaking points are converging with gut-wrenching speed: orca starve, salmon diminish, cedar trees are parched, standing skeletons of their former selves, as smoke fills the summer sky.

I once harboured the hope that the photographs I make would be a small legacy of some sort, the delving of one person, alive during the great turning, leaving messages for an unknown future.

I now realise that future will, in all likelihood, not exist.

What is it to face the clear-eyed truth of the planet's situation, this great decline of Life itself, at what seems to be simultaneously the highest and lowest point of our human history? How does one adjust to the loss of personal, familial and cultural legacy?

I suspect there will be no adjustment possible in the coming years, no time to ingest the losses, before the next wash over us in mounting waves of decline. It will be task enough to simply remain a conscious witness to all we have wrought.

Note

1. Albrecht G., Sartore G.M., Connor L., Higginbotham N., Freeman S., Kelly B., Stain H., Tonna A., Pollard G., *Australas Psychiatry,* 2007

Rob Carney

A Rough Draft of Ten New Commandments

1. There's a road sign along I-70
near the Utah/Colorado border

that says, 'Travel
Through Time'.

I didn't exit, though.
I figured it wasn't being literal,

just giving directions
to a byway

through eons of rock,
past vast striations layered

like chapters in *The Book of This Planet*, yes,
but I wouldn't actually be exiting 2019.

2. I was driving back from Ridgway, Colorado,
this townful

of Arts District patrons.
You should go.

Early March.
They call it 'Mud Season' there,

like it's spring's first flower or crop,
like Ridgway is the place mud aims for

in its annual migration, herding in
or winging down

then getting busy
with some serious breeding:

mud displays
to spark female attention,

mud challengers
to last year's champion,

mud anthems and warbles
and bugle calls –

they named it right.
The yards and streets were muddy.

3. It might be one of those weird things while driving,
when it's hours of your own thoughts

and not much else,
but the Colorado Plateau buttes and mesas

seem to move, to float along
west-northwest,

a barnacled armada.
This isn't the ocean; I know that.

The smoke rising up from those mesas
is only clouds;

that's the sky,
it's only overcast, but still…

maybe all the sagebrush dotted around
could be bison if they'd just stand up,

if they'd just quit kneeling
and stampede,

or graze,
or walk on over here and hijack the freeway;

if it took all day for them to cross, I wouldn't mind.
I could wait for that miracle.

4. Here's what I mean about patrons:
The people of Ridgway have filled their town

with poems.
They're painted on metal

and bolted to walls. There's a map,
you can tour them and read,

like walking around in a book,
a book with a binding of sky,

and trees,
and a cat

stretched out on a windowsill lit up with sun.
We could use a lot more of this.

Town after town.
A whole library.

5. According to *The Book of This Planet*,
we haven't been bad,

at least not for algae. It's blooming
all over the ocean; it's doing

quite well, kicking ass
in our river mouths;

focus on that.
Don't think about dead-zones,

think about blooming.
Blooms feed bees.

6. *from page 2019…*

… not the Year of the Polar Bear.
They're searching for seals in our towns now,

looking for sea-ice
in our kitchens,

our dumpsters; good luck.
That isn't where we're hiding the horizon.

And it isn't the Whale's Year either.
At least not whales in the Philippines:

stomachs so full
of plastic bags

there's no room left.
Not even for krill.

7. The last tiger is somewhere
   in our future.

8. The last elephant
   is somewhere in our future.

9. The last uncut slope of cedar –
   in our future.

   Like we're rain.
   Like the rest

   is just sediment
   washing away.

10. *Mud vs. Not-Mud*

    My Maine Coon cat, he's mud.
    He's got a new way of going outside,

    stalking in a circle
    round the chair

    while I open the door,
    then a *lunge-dash* past me

    out to the porch. What is he practicing?
    I don't know, but I know it's mud.

    And I know sharks are mud.
    May the oceans increase with their teeth.

To anyone who'd kill them for their fins –
you're not mud at all;

there's mud and there's slime,
and there's a difference.

The sound of Louisiana thunder: mud.
The sound of ice in a glass…

it's hot, or you're thirsty,
or there's company over: good mud.

Not mud: all the bought politicians.
Not mud: all the goddamn guns.

Mud is the woods' slow
reaching. Green

and skyward.
Travelling through time.

Thomas Keyes

God's Own Alphabet

INPRINCIPIOERATUERBUM

The alphabet that washed up on the shores of Ireland in the fifth century was characteristically Roman and contained almost all the symbols in use today, with only minor alterations. If words could be plucked from the flowing river of a classical Latin *scriptio continua* manuscript they could be set into this book's computer-generated sequence of symbols with a misleading degree of comfort by the modern reader of text. The original scribe, however, wouldn't recognise the arrangement, for although the Romans were already many centuries into the history of writing, the word as a physically separated unit did not yet exist. The form of writing that we know, and the type of reading we use to decipher it, began their development not in the centre of civilisation but at the end of the earth, on an island without cities, with an alphabet that wasn't adopted as an aid to memory or administration but venerated as the word of God incarnate.

This essay follows the alphabet from its arrival in Ireland with Saint Patrick, to its adoption in New York by the graffiti subculture – a form in which it returned, in 1983, to Belfast, just a few miles from where it had first landed 1500 years earlier. Graffiti writing is a craft and for much of its history the alphabet was primarily a tool of another craft, that of the scribe. The parallels in style, technique and even social organisation between a modern graffiti writer and an early medieval scribe illuminator are striking. Less obvious are the incremental steps between the flowering of these two letter crafts, and their cumulative impact on how we read and think. Though the alphabetic symbols have barely altered, the layout of the text and the mind that deciphers it have both changed radically. This is an attempt to understand these shifts – from a scribe's perspective.

Insular Majuscule

The alphabet's first recorded outings in fifth-century Ireland, carried in books by Christian missionaries preaching the Gospel, were precarious: by his own account, Patrick was repeatedly threatened and extorted for bribes. Without even remnants of Roman bureaucracy to graft the alphabet onto, it had to be planted straight into an oral Iron Age society by attaching it to the Christian stories it carried. Eventually, this worked. Little more than a century after these first encounters, kings were vying for Patrick's patronage and books were being carried into battle for their apotropaic properties. Ancient geometric designs, embellishing the fine metalwork worn by the kings who had threatened Patrick, started appearing on Irish manuscripts. They led to the 'carpet pages' of the seventh to ninth centuries, that appeared almost woven in their complex detail.

Once they'd taken it on, the Irish were not shy in adapting and developing the alphabet. Some of the simplest and most complex innovations ever to occur in the art of letter writing are products of early medieval Ireland. The most familiar of these innovations are *distinctiones*, the spaces between words. This is the beginning of the modern text, along with punctuation, chapters and references. Such devices were biblical study aids, but what they allowed for was the expansion of the alphabet into other domains: literally, taking words out of context. By the end of the sixth century the Irish language was co-opted into the alphabet. Ireland's pagan oral history was recorded, the legal profession published texts on everything from murder to the trespass of bees, and copies of the classics from across Europe were hunted down and transcribed. The Irish monastic schools became the Ivy League of the literate world.

Looking at the writing style and layout of a typical eighth-century *Insular Majuscule* text, however, practicality doesn't appear to be the intention. The generous text spacing would be considered decadent in a modern book. These texts were written on calfskin vellum, each blank surface representing hours of labour on a valuable material. Today it would be cheaper to write on £20 notes covering the same surface area than to produce the equivalent standard of vellum under the same conditions. The script itself, written by scribes many years into their craft, flows in a manner that belies its complexity. These are not a series of fixed letter-forms that simply change their sequence for each word; the connections between letters are given as much attention as the letters themselves, giving endless subtle variety to maintain overall balance. This is not a script that can be dissected and usurped into print.

For all the attention lavished on the script, though – more than in any other writing culture before or until recently since – the letters are not trusted to deliver the message alone. The word is yet to become the dominant form of expression; thoughts do not spontaneously form grammatical sentences inside minds. Insular Majuscule rests on the vellum within a geometric plane, and when both text and geometry appear overtly on the same page, it's clear what the governing force is. The letters submit to the underlying web set by compass and straight edge; words yield to the ancient craft of bringing forth an image through geometry.

Insular Minuscule

However lavish these manuscripts appear to modern eyes, the primary motivation for some innovations was to save time. This is how Insular Minuscule was developed, from the Roman cursive script known as Half Uncial, with enough style added to make it palatable to the Irish while still being less cumbersome than Insular Majuscule.

Compared to its predecessor, this script is a pleasure to write. Letters have fewer strokes so require fewer pen lifts, and there is little variation in the ways letters are attached. Most of the necessary shapes can be achieved by twisting the nib or alternating pressure. Scribes were beginning to tread a fine line, as the pressures of time and, later, money, forced speed on the craftsman. Each script that emerged over the coming centuries was an attempt by its creators to keep pace with the ever-increasing speed of production while not sacrificing the beauty of the craft. It was the offspring of an Insular Minuscule script that became the reigning style in Europe and carried the written word into the Middle Ages.

Luxeuil Minuscule

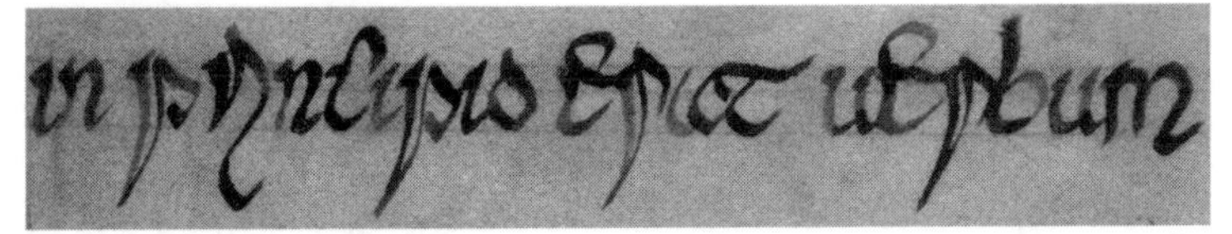

The Irish monk Columbanus set out from Bangor monastery on the shores of Belfast Lough to arrive in Gaul around 590, wanting to re-establish the waning influence of Christianity after the collapse of Rome. He travelled throughout Europe founding monasteries, advising kings, rebuking popes and writing lengthy letters on church doctrine and issues of the day, as well as poetry and hymns. One of his monasteries in Gaul, built on the ruins of the former Roman fort of Luxovium, was Luxeuil. It became the most famous monastery of the age, its school attracting the sons of kings from all over Europe. Columbanus was later exiled after his criticism of the ruling dynasty but the monastery he founded continued to thrive, producing its own script, Luxeuil Minuscule.

The script is a classic 'charter hand', designed for legal charters and sensitive documentation. It was deliberately difficult to read for those not familiar with it, yet surprisingly quick to write. The forms that appear most complex are composites of several letters combined that contain fewer strokes than the same letters written separately.

Corbie Minuscule

Corbie, a daughter house of Luxeuil, developed its own version of this script, which later caught the eye of the Northumbrian monk Alcuin. As one of Charlemagne's closest advisors, he was given the task of standardising Latin script and pronunciation across the Holy Roman Empire. The Emperor never mastered Latin himself but was aware of the reputation of the Irish schools. So in the ninth century, for the first time, an education policy was developed. Based on the work of ascetics in monastic clusters of rural mud huts, it still forms the basic principle of state-endorsed learning. Corbie Minuscule became Carolingian Minuscule and would take the alphabet into the Gothic era.

The Irish monks may have believed the alphabet to be sacred but they didn't entrust writing with the mystical capabilities and monopoly over thought that we grant it today. The well-ordered, spaced-out text with its neat cursive options that had developed to spread the light of God, now escaped from its ascetic parents. Having been introduced by the church into the royal courts of Europe – and as the church itself became a land-owning bureaucracy and political power-broker – the alphabet turned ugly and grew up to dominate all of society, willingly literate or not.

The incursion began with an obscure ritual developed within the Irish church during the years in which it remained outside the administrative control of Rome. This period lasted from the arrival of Patrick in the fifth century until the Synod of Whitby in 664, when King Oswiu favoured the Roman argument over the Irish for the calculation of

Easter. The Irish version of confession, however, survived. Known as The Sacrament of Penance and Reconciliation, it prepared the minds of the congregation to be read as books. Columbanus himself may have introduced this ritual into Europe, where it was later adopted by the medieval Catholic Church. The old public rituals of penance for sin were now internalised. Images of the Book of Judgment appeared on church walls, reminding everyone that their inner thoughts could become text. Thoughts and words were becoming inseparable. The congregation could be persuaded to believe their thoughts could be 'read', and the alphabet could move towards excluding the unwritten entirely.

In England, the total victory of the alphabet over the mind occurred on 3rd September 1189. This date, the coronation of Richard I, was retrospectively established nearly a century later as the boundary of 'time immemorial': the legal limit of memory. Reaching back beyond that date, your legal claim was considered to be established. From that date onwards, though, documentary evidence was required to settle a dispute in court. There had for some time been a legal limit on memory but it had shifted to allow for the mortality of those who possessed the memory. Now, preserved in writing, artificial memory was made legally necessary, and thus made permanent. The alphabet didn't just have a life of its own; it had become immortal, independent of God, his scribes and the geometric artwork that had questioned its supremacy.

The scribes did not benefit from the proliferation of their craft. The legendary saints and scholars of the Insular period, working from divine inspiration, were largely replaced in the Middle Ages by lay scribes in workshops, earning a farm labourer's wage. The Insular style disappeared, and despite the aesthetic appeal of many later manuscripts, the techniques used were often just time-saving artists' tricks. Quickly-drawn vines with no formal rules and dabs of pigment for leaves replaced the geometric meditation of a day spent unfurling the tree of life in a minutely detailed border.

The spread of the word beyond the monastery walls and into the management of the lives of everyday people also had a profound effect on the script. As documentation proliferated, parchment became scarce. Its quality declined and a tighter script was developed to fit more words on the page. *Distinctiones* were too ingrained to do away with, so the spaces within the letters themselves had to be sacrificed. This was the beginning of the early Gothic scripts that were the workhorse of the Renaissance, before being captured and set into type.

Gothic Textura

m principio erat verbum et....

There is no definitive Gothic script. Its styles varied with region, workshop and individual. No matter how lowly the status of the average scribe, it appears that the need to be creative with the quill did not diminish. While the pressure to fit more words onto the page is obvious, the lack of compromise on style is, to my eye, impressive. It was this final phase of development, creating compact letters that could be joined without any variation, which opened the way for the typesetter.

Until this point, the tool marks of the individual maker of a script had shaped each letter, in a relationship paralleled in all other material crafts. In the mid-1400s, however, Gutenberg's development of typeset print turned the already deconsecrated alphabet into the first mass-produced, standardised product of culture. The alphabet always had the potential to become a medium to transmit many thoughts; now it had taken a leap forward in the march to dominance over all thought.

From set type to digital fonts

In principio erat verbum

The Renaissance and the Reformation spread chaos and information in equal measure around Europe at a speed that society was ill-equipped to cope with. Proto-states coalesced around increasingly refined vernacular languages. The religion once held together by a book split over its own doctrine, awaiting dissection by the newly emerging sciences. The handwritten books of the medieval period had been so laborious to produce, that popes and kings wanting to ban a heretical text could realistically order every single copy to be destroyed. Those days had gone. Three hundred years into the age of print, the alphabet was still causing trouble, printed in pamphlets that roused the mob to revolution in France. In 1798 many of Luxeuil's manuscripts were destroyed when peasants burned the monastic libraries to rid them of title deeds that they believed still made them serfs on the monasteries' lands. Faith in the power of the word had come full circle in a millennium of European upheaval.

Beyond this point the alphabet becomes so pervasive as to appear benign, and by the 20th century it was the obvious code with which to label the components of our DNA. The developmental trail of the human-sculpted handicraft that we have been following goes cold. By the 1970s, it's fair to say, there wasn't much else to be expected from the scribal tradition. The printing press, after centuries of supremacy, was about to lose to computers. Fonts were to be co-opted into the digital revolution and the odd bit of advertising work might be thrown to the calligraphically-minded designer. Scripts entered churches, but only on crumpled wedding invitations.

Ladybird Book of Handwriting

In principio erat verbum

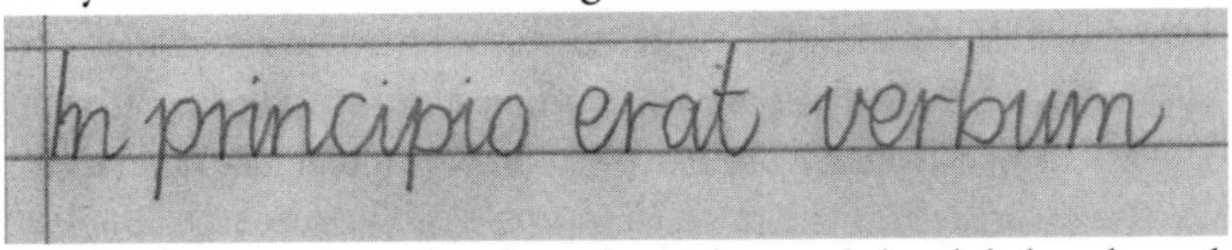

Yet the unbroken line of scribes who had carried the alphabet through the last millennium of development continued. As the first cumbersome computers were nearly ready to enter the classroom, millions of children still sat and learned the now ancient craft of handwriting. The sentiments of Columbanus and the regular strokes of Alcuin flowed in this faint glimmer of an archaic ritual long-parted from its heyday of saints and scholars, battle books and carpet pages. The *Ladybird Book of Handwriting* treated the children of the late 1960s as if the Victorian invention of the modern concept of childhood had never taken root. They were reinstated as apprentices in the craft of their culture and were not patronised: 'The ballpoint pen is... most emphatically discouraged.' It was in New York and Philadelphia that children first took this craft out of the classroom and onto the streets.

Graffiti

The debate still simmers as to whether graffiti is an art or a crime. In the early 1970s it was neither. In 1971 a reporter tracked down a recent high school graduate who featured prominently in this strange new phenomenon, and the interview with Taki 183 in the *New York Times* turned this niche hobby into a vocation for a generation of New York's youth, by demonstrating the simplicity of the concept and the status of the protagonist. It soon became an expensive problem, its criminality elevated from misdemeanour to felony. Participants were quick to realise the limitations of the letter-writing techniques that had survived to be passed down to them through education. With so many people involved in graffiti writing the words no longer stood out, and the competition to reign through style began.

By the mid1970s, less than a decade from its inception, the graffiti-writing subculture had a range of writing styles, embellishment techniques and an accompanying lexicon and code of conduct that cannot have been surpassed since the scriptorium that produced the Book of Kells was active. The master scribes of this new incarnation were known as the style kings. Their achievements and innovations were recognised, named and attributed. Hondo painted the first top to bottom train carriage, Kase2 invented computer rock style. The scriptoriums were now in the train yards; the scribes formed into crews that took on apprentices for schooling in the craft. The subculture used both missions and patronage to spread, the art world's brief fascination with graffiti lasting long enough to fund its expansion into Europe. *Style Wars* won the Sundance Film Festival Grand Jury Prize for Documentary In 1983; the book *Subway Art* became a bestseller. The alphabet, it seemed, could be brought back into human hands.

But graffiti is just one small offshoot of the evolution of letter styles and it is not immune to the alphabet's seemingly irrepressible growth towards the new light of our culture. For the current generation of writers the toolkit has expanded beyond spray paint, gloves and bolt cutters to include an iPhone, as a train now only needs to run on Instagram to get up. Paper, the last physical manifestation of the alphabet, now seems comfortingly nostalgic compared to its new digital domain. The individuality of bespoke parchment codices and the quirks of a scribe's hand giving shape to the letters are now reversed, as targeted streaming of advertising and digital platforms allow the modern literate to construct an identity like assembling flat-pack furniture, consuming fragments of set type that can be curated and discarded. A monoculture of digital 'individuality' now thrives as if independent of the physical world, without the need for apprenticeship, study or responsibility.

In entering the post-truth era the alphabet has finally broken free of its roots. It was supported first by God, then by facts, but always within a cultural value system of learning. Now alternative facts compete on an equal platform for entry into the literate mind, without any gatekeepers. For all the written word's achievements and pitfalls over the centuries, the mistrust it can now inspire has not been seen since its mythical inception.

The Egyptian legend about the invention of letters by the ibis-headed god Thoth came with a warning. King Thamus turns down the offer of the alphabet as a memory aid for his subjects, claiming that it 'will train ignorant know-alls, nosey know-nothings, boring wiseacres'. Standing in an oral culture, it was easy for the king to see the alphabet from the outside and recognise its limitations. We don't have that viewpoint, nor can we turn down the offer our ancestors accepted. We interpret the world through a prism created by the decisions of successive generations of writers, some of which have had profound effects on how we think and engage with the world. Just as we have gained enough information to know what our culture is doing to the Earth, we have lost the ability to collectively interpret it in anything beyond an analytical manner. Our increasing reliance upon the great craft of our culture has dulled our other senses. The linear march of historical time pinned down in written history distorts our perception of the cycles and rhythms of nature. Stories that are no longer fixed to landscapes and their varied inhabitants leave us with a homogeneity of abstract human voices. Yet the words I am using to construct these sentences remain, for most of us, the only medium through which to articulate the concept of a loss we are ill-equipped to define.

Thoth's letters are a pharmakon, a medicine or a poison depending on the translation and possibly the dose. This alphabet is not a benign set of symbols that simply aid the transmission of that which already exists, nor is it an all-encompassing mode of expression that can encode all of creation. What the alphabet becomes is – at least for now – still under the influence of its users, for if the AI evangelists get their singularity there will be no return. As this civilisation declines we will remain immersed in letters, as will the many cultures that have been forced to take them up. Literacy, once planted, has proven impossible to uproot or even control but it has at times been carefully tended. In between tyrannical technological and ideological growth spurts there have been unexpected flowerings and fresh shoots emerging at the edges. The future could once again emerge in the margins, with those who are trying to replant the alphabet as one craft among many, with roots, limitations and contradictions.

References

Clanchy, M.T., *From Memory to Written Record: England 1066–1307*, Blackwell, 2nd edition, 1993.

Cooper, Martha and Chalfant, Henry, *Subway Art*, Thames and Hudson, 1985.

Drogin, Marc, *Medieval Calligraphy: Its History and Technique*, Dover, 1989.

Gourdie, Tom, *The Ladybird Book of Handwriting*, Wills and Hepworth, 1968.

Illich, Ivan and Sanders, Barry, *ABC: The Alphabetization of the Popular Mind*, Penguin, 1988.

Ó Cróinín, Dáibhí, *Early Medieval Ireland*, Routledge, 2nd edition, 2017.

Ó Fiaich, Tomás, *Columbanus in His Own Words*, Veritas, 2012.

Patterson, Nerys, *Cattle Lords and Clansmen: The Social Structure of Early Ireland,* Notre Dame Press, 2nd edition, 2012.

Saint Patrick, *The Confession of Saint Patrick*, translated by Wright, Rev. Charles, Dalcassian, 2017.

Neale Inglenook

At the Birth of an Age

It was a long time ago, this stone was born. It began in the blood heat of the mantle, flowing and unsolid, not yet separate. By the force of its mother's body, by its own heat and mass, it rose, cooling and coalescing, pushed out from the centre, through the opening in the stone skin of the Earth. Becoming what it would be, veins and nodes of crystal steadily hardening, settling into its firmness. At last jutting upward, out of the greater planet, feeling on its skin the waves of the exterior world.

Still held against the heat of its mother below it, this stone is blanketed with sediment and lime. This mountain floats on the sea of its future kin, the molten rock, the whirling power of igneous tides. It is not free of that force, it is at the point of contact and friction. It is already being torn apart.

The rains and glaciers come, gouging deep canyons in its faces. The tireless ocean tears at its feet. The great masses of stone to which it belongs are ramming against one another, pushing one down into the molten heat, heaving up the other, rending mountains.

In the tectonic shift, this rock is shorn from the rest of its body, and begins its grinding exodus northward. The ceaseless waters and ice wear at it, pressures all around abrade it. Steadily worn away, it loses parts of itself to boulder, pebble, sand, silt. It endures. For this it was made.

Waves of lichens and grasses, animals and forests, flow over it. They leave the layered imprint of their vanished forms. The glaciers grow and recede, grow and recede, pulsing in decline. At last they disappear, remembered only in the cool winter snow on the peaks.

Northward slides the granite, with its compatriots of sandstone and limestone on its flanks. Redwoods fur its deep canyons, woody shrubs struggle roots into its tenuous hillsides. The gaunt cypresses clutch the crags of its rocky points where they meet the endless breakers.

The granite stone is here. It is this coast.

1919

The unrelenting waves roll in and quarry out boulders from the little cove beneath the headland. They lie half-buried in the sand of their own granite body. All around is the low shush of the water, the primordial scent of kelp.

Suddenly, they move, they are borne up the cliff with hot speed, are raised and set upon their sister outcrops. Mortared in place, formed around a space, a den, a house.

Within is the quick blood-beat of the ocean swells. The dexterous mammalian hands against the granite's rough hide. The steady murmur of voices, and radiant warmth, not felt since the stones lay deep in the hot dark of the planet. The sounds and the heat work deep into their hearts.

The stones are spoken to, they are seen and loved. Poetry is read to them and seeps into them, the vibrations of the voices saying poetry resonate inside, until the stones themselves are made poetry. The walls are poetry, and poetry is made stone, standing in warm walls around the hearth on the headland, battered by the sea wind but solid and still for now.

2009

I fall to my knees beside a black lake. Minnesota night near midsummer, waft of cold algae, splintered planks of the dock under my palms. Opaque trees edge the distant stars. My heart in a seizure of grief whose grip will never ease.

I have been divorced for almost a year. My best friend has just been married. This is supposed to be a joyful moment, but I am alone on a dock in the dark, unable to stand under the weight of loss.

My friend will stay here while I return to San Francisco, a city buried in cloud. I have a new love, but my insides are like a burn scar after a wildfire, black stick trees and ash underfoot. They won't give what she needs, she is already beginning to sense it.

Sending myself back to that moment, alone on the dock, the cold breath of lake mud and the chirping summer darkness around me, I have no idea what is in my future.

1919

Before they break ground on the house, he holds a ceremony. On the headland where they will build, the granite outcrops thrust up through the midden left by native people. Now there is lupine and coastal sage covering the black loam and mussel shells, built up here by thousands of years of habitation.

Their life is still here, intermingled with the yet more ancient life of the granite. He sees the shining shards of broken shell, the scars of fire on the rock.

He is just beginning his true work. The place has penetrated his learned, civilised veneer. Already he sees the granite has a life, millions upon millions of years long. He speaks to it: *A hundred years, two hundred, / You have been dissevered from humanity…no one / Touched you with love…*[1]

He lays his hand on the stone. The coarse crystals and lichen rasp his palm. The wind comes buffeting off the waves.

To the rock, to the perdurable life of the place, he brings an offering. He pours wine and milk and honey onto the stone. These symbols, good things that humans can take in: the succour of a mother's breast, the sweetness that is sustenance and delight, the warmth of libation. *I did not dream,* he will write later, *the taste of wine could bind with granite,* but the small gift shows his recognition of *the stone / Endurance that is waiting millions of years to carry / A corner of the house, this also destined.*[2]

His hand on the rock, the sweet offering runnelling down, he can feel the vague shape of the future around him, the house he will build. And he senses the inertia of history, the long cyclical tides of the Earth's movement, that brought him and the granite to this place, at this time. They are both embedded in this vast earthly churning, the stone in the arc from magma to mountain to this headland, the poet in the successive waves of human animals, growing and reproducing and dying, flowing over the continents. These cycles have drawn them together; he acknowledges and sacralises them.

The gulls cry, and the breeze sweeps the headland with the scent of cold brine.

…this also destined…

2009

I sit on the fissured granite, on the rocky shore beneath the house. Grey breakers sweep in, thunder and spume under a clouded sky. This land endlessly tearing itself apart, intense feeling in the ocean's movement, in the stone's endurance.

A year since my marriage ended, and before that, my father-in-law fell from a cliff on this coast, as if taken for a sacrifice. My grandmother has just had a stroke; like a mountain being ground to sand, she is dissipating until she will no longer be herself.

Sometimes I go numb, don't tremble with loss, but these times are few. So I come here, where the naked granite destroys the waves as they sweep in, and is steadily worn away. Where the raw feeling of the world is bare, and where I am not alone.

In the offices and classrooms of the university where I have been studying and teaching, showing this feeling is not appropriate. It is not appropriate in almost any interaction in the cityscape except for the most intimate. There I am trapped beneath pavement. There, I am like the living land and all its beings, covered over and denied, their wounds unacknowledged. Self-important humanity blotting them out.

Here, I am a feeling body amidst the greater feeling. Here is the poet's house, and his spirit, a dark smoulder in the granite.

1919

The Armistice is less than a year old. The twins are three. He is building the house for his family. He goes down through summer flowers to the margin of the sea, where the thick swells wash in and withdraw. He and the stonemason dredge up boulders from the coarse sand, and settle them in the walls, where they will lie for a century and more.

He is making a stone house out of the bones of the Earth and writing parables to last a thousand years. The headland is hardly built upon; the intensity of the place is unfiltered; it sweeps in with every wave onto the crags of stone.

The radio has squawked its dire news for years. By the end, the war killed 13 million. It's twin catastrophe, influenza, 22 million. Swathes of Europe are scorched earth soaked in blood. Scent of an apocalyptic fire on the wind.

It is hard for the poet to ignore the radio. He writes, *You making haste haste on decay…*[3]

Building, sweating, his muscles and tendons straining. Being his body. In these times his mind gains something, not peace, not order, but a sense of solidity, of being righted on its axis. The glimmering ocean and stolid continent and huge ephemeral clouds are bodies living and feeling, beyond all measure. His barest intuition of it is heartbreaking.

Una brings the boys to see the rising walls, and like sprites they run across the foundations, where he has wedded the stone.

2009

It comes out of my mouth before I know what I am saying: *my body yearns to hold its child.* The ghost of the small form pressing into my chest.

I am with a friend in a dim bar, where we come to commiserate over our raw hearts. For a moment she puts down her beer, probes the dark between us. My friend is seeking across this space, full of shadows and drunken chatter, the visceral sense of what I feel.

There are few words to be said. I am divorced and my current love doesn't want children. There is no way to know if my body's need can ever be fulfilled. The ocean mist is thick on the ground.

I am with my former self and my friend, sitting with them like a shade. If I could speak, I could tell them: you, friend, will move far from this city you love; you will find an agent and publish a novel; your marriage will dissolve. I will cross the continent by bicycle, live on a sailboat, move for two years to Korea, work as a farmhand. I will fall in love again, we will get married, we will have two children.

But they can only feel the barest outline of me beside them. The future is the fog-shrouded night.

1919

This moment of the world holds within it all the future beauties and horrors.

The century of human vulgarities, the grey breakers of November storms, the white gulls dancing with the moon. The twins growing, becoming men, coming home from war, grandchildren running wild in the garden.

From this vantage point he can foresee nothing in detail. The mass movements of humanity are there to be charted through history like the tides – the ledger won't tell him the names of demagogues or tyrants, or what year they will arise, only that they will come.

2019

I sit on the shore beneath the house. I brush my palms over the rough stone that has endured here for millions of years. I have come to touch it after all this time; I have come to feel the spirit in the stone again.

I am trying to quiet my mind. My radio has been spewing horrors, just as it did a hundred years ago. Like needles to the bone: a father and daughter face down in the mud of the Rio Grande; black trees in a tornado of flame; a whale carcass rolling in the waves.

I close my eyes, steeple my hands. Feel the primal granite under me, going down and down, hear the wash of the surf. The salt wind eddies between my palms.

We have two young children, like the poet and his wife a hundred years hence. Our second daughter is just over a month old. Among our little family we have love, and caring. And we have food to eat and a safe place to live.

With a deep aching love comes the fear of its loss. There are commonplace dangers, and more distant, the black clouds of the future, looming perils from which, I fear, I cannot protect our daughters.

I have chosen / Being, says the poet from the rock, *therefore wounds, bonds, limits and pain; the crowded mind and the / anguished nerves, experience and ecstasy.*[4]

1919

The house is built. On winter nights after the boys are asleep, and the gales howl at the windows, he drinks whiskey with Una by the fire. They lean their heads close to speak, *about love and death…nothing more timely, nothing less real.*[5] The house surrounds them in dark redwood and the hard shining granite of the shore.

He has placed a bed in the guest room, beside the rock he anointed. He already knows it will be his deathbed, and Una's too. When and how, he cannot see. But the great turnings make some things certain if not transparent.

Meanwhile, all the joy and beauty in his life will come from things close at hand. The attentive touch for a child or a stone, talks in the night with Una, the solid walls of the house, his honest words on the page, the endless waves maned with spume, his wild coast.

Dear old poet, at the birth of what age did you attend? This troubled time when the more-than-human world is in upheaval, when this civilisation grinds like a mountain along the edge of the continent, crumbling apart. The breakdown you predicted has not come all at once; we are still in that dark passage.

There remains this question: how to live well, faced with these grave certainties? As a kind of answer, I might distill a credo from what I have learned from you: be tender with children, ferocious as a hawk in art, and meld the spirit with the thousand epochs of the granite.

2019

I sit again on the shore beneath the poet's house. Golden sun on the sculpted stone, the little waves lapping over the outcrops. Pelicans and cormorants stand on their islands, wings folded and bills to chest. The seaweeds brush languidly through water like sea glass.

The headland has been covered over with thousands of mansions. One is built upon the very granite of the shore below the poet's house. Even now there are trucks bringing construction materials, engines roaring, the high grinding whine of a diamond saw cutting stone.

He speaks to me: ... *does it care? / Not faintly. It has all time. It knows the people are a tide / That swells and in time will ebb, and all / their works dissolve. Meanwhile the image of the pristine beauty / Lives in the very grain of the granite...*[6]

The human noise has quieted. The sound of water washing the rock, shushing in the beach gravel. I turn, and I see the boys, playing in the waves.

I see them the way I see the wind. Not with my eyes. I feel them. Their image is unbidden and perfectly clear. They are still here, and they are speaking to me.

I don't see Una, but I know she is near, watching over the children. And the poet, their father, Robinson, is in the house he built for them, facing east so he won't be distracted by the immense beauty of the ocean, putting pen to paper.

3019

A calm day on this bay. They glide around the headland in their boat, drop the sail and drag the hull onto a silty bar by the river mouth. They fill the water filters and hang them to drip through the wood-grain to the crocks below. The children run up the hill with their sticks, chasing the headland rabbits from the sagebrush. The adults follow. There are silvered tree trunks on the ground, beside the stones upthrust like broken teeth. Down by the point, the tide draws outward, and there is a square foundation of granite, almost worn away. They stand looking at it, and the foamy swells and white gulls, the warbled mirror of the sea, and wonder, who was it who lived here?

Notes

1. Jeffers, Robinson, 'To The Rock That Will Be A Cornerstone Of The House', *The Selected Poetry of Robinson Jeffers*, Stanford University Press, 2001, p. 21.
2. Ibid.
3. 'Shine, Perishing Republic', ibid., p. 23.
4. 'from At The Birth Of An Age', ibid., pp. 506–507.
5. 'For Una', ibid., pp. 565–567.
6. ibid.

Samantha M. Harvey

These Waters are Patient

On 22nd December 2018, I stop on a sidewalk in New York City to look at the moon. It is a full moon, large in the sky, yet to stare it straight in the face I have to stand in a specific spot, hold my head very still, and aim my gaze between the silhouettes of buildings.

Hold that image. The moon. The sidewalk. Let's instead skip to 21st April 2018, when I walk out of a nearby drugstore with a pregnancy test in my pocket.

Must I really make myself the protagonist of this story, as we humans are wont to do? Let's resist that habit. Let's instead talk about what was, what could have been, what will be. Let's talk about early colonisation of the New World, about flocks of birds so dense they blocked the sun, the lakes and streams so full of fish you could just reach in and grab one, the miles and miles and miles of dense forest.

Let's talk about time:

Forty-six weeks since I dipped one plastic applicator in pee and
the other in water, just to be sure
Three hundred thousand years for a rock by the shore
to wear down to sand
Nine years since the moment I decide never to have a baby

On 6th August 2010 I board a plane to Miami where I meet my parents and sister for a long-planned vacation. We warm our feet on the sand and walk into the ocean, which we all agree feels as docile as bath-water, unreconcilable with the violent images on the news. There's been an explosion at sea just 600 miles away, two million gallons of crude oil billowing out of the ocean floor every day for months with no real plan to stop it, pundits claiming the ocean will 'self-clean'. Watching the water from the beach it is tempting to believe them, but then I think of the bluefin tuna arriving to spawn in this toxic slop, the strongest, wiliest ones on their 6,000-mile journey, the ones who have eluded high-priced plates at sushi restaurants, and I wonder if it's even moral to catch a little swim by the shore. It is on this beach, sliding so easefully into the oily foulness of that water, that I decide I'll never have children. This decision makes it easier to enjoy the swim.

Twenty-eight weeks since the last day possible to get an abortion
in the state of New York
One point five seconds for a small handful of sand to fall through
five fingers
Three hundred and ninety years since Puritan John Endicott
took charge of Massachusetts Bay

Let's talk about the people who took and took and took so much it was never enough, who demonised indigenous folks, swore Satan lurked in the woods and made up the rules of dominance that got themselves rich. Let's talk about concrete, traffic jams and plastic trinkets.

Let's talk about a book I start reading in February 2019, *Facing West: The Metaphysics of Indian-Hating and Empire Building*, by a historian called Richard Drinnon. The book is 467 pages long but may as well stop after 34 because I am reading the first chapter at a snail's pace, repeating sentences over and over, stopping to attend to cries and gurgles, catching streams of drool before they reach the blanket, hoisting my tired body out of bed to lift the baby, pad to the kitchen and carefully warm ounces of milk. I read somewhere that hearing as many words as possible in a baby's first year helps with brain development. So I plop her on the bed, scratch her little feet and read aloud the books I'd planned to read before she was born.

Drinnon's been in my collection for years, recommended by an activist I met while supporting some environmental justice work near the Texas-Mexico border. But this book is dense and violent, so I've guiltily carried it through multiple apartment moves, jamming it up high among the reference volumes, assuming I already knew, more or less, the truths revealed inside, as if its mere presence in my home were enough. But suddenly this old book calls from the shelves with fresh urgency. Perhaps by speaking the history I never heard as a child, perhaps by telling my daughter the truth from the very beginning, I can help her shift something. Perhaps a pathway to some sort of reconciliation starts with this book on this bed in the New York City winter of 2019.

Sixty-nine years since atmospheric carbon rose above its highest level in pre-industrial times
Four hundred and fifty years for the plastic applicator of a drug-store pregnancy test to degrade, but never fully disappear
Two hundred thousand years since the first Homo sapiens *walked the earth of Southern Africa*

Early pages focus on a battle between the Puritan Endicott and a maypole-dancing infidel named Thomas Morton who celebrates nature and, for the crime of trading with the natives, is reviled and deported twice back to England, on one of these occasions dragged aboard an eastbound ship as the colonial leadership destroys his maypole and sets his home ablaze. They burn it to the ground before the boat pushes off to ensure Morton will see it crumble. The cheerful tone and soft cadence required to read this gruesome history to a baby give it a fairy-tale quality, and a certain dark magic fills the room. The baby's unencumbered gaze slides above and behind my head, exploring the humid green of the pre-industrial land, watching the maypole ribbons, the burning house, the fleeing wildlife, the thwarted man dragged away in shackles.

Eighty years until daily floods will make lower Manhattan uninhabitable

The sidewalks of New York City are weathered and uneven in places. Muted colors of fossilised chewing gum form archipelagos on the concrete. Names hastily scratched in wet cement announce histories of love, trace the human need to hold on, to be seen and remembered. When she cries, I wrap the baby to my chest in the manner women have been doing for millennia, using a long, flexible cloth now mass-marketed on Amazon.com to the descendants of Endicott for $39.99. Walking the sidewalks quiets her. I look down expecting to see her fuzzy head burrowed and sleeping, but instead there is her face – serious, alert, her tiny eyes blinking and shifting from place to place to place. What must she make of this place, so removed from the nature that brought her here?

Seventy-eight point six years until the average woman born in the US in 2018 will die

Massachusetts can be reached in a morning's drive, but in the 1600s the two lands must have seemed distant and remote. Could anyone at the time have believed the space between would ever disappear, and along with it all the quiet spots to listen, to think, to consider, to feel? Could they have felt the true weight of their footprints on this land, understood the consequences of an unexamined idea, imagined what a baby born in 2019 might face? A time that must have felt so ordained by the will of God now seems just another time, just another group of people who happened to be there in that moment, people who simply could have made the decision to do something else.

Twenty-eight months since the US government shot rubber bullets and tear gas at indigenous water protectors at Standing Rock

As for Morton, who knows what he was really like? Trained to read history as a series of leaders and saviours, I am tempted to view him as the alternate universe, the road not taken, the path to a less punitive, less anthropocentric future. But reality isn't so cut and dried. A white man of his time, it's probable Morton engaged in his fair share of bigotry; a Morton-led colony would still have been a colony, after all.

But the baby and I allow ourselves to imagine a bit. As I read to her, the Morton who materialises above our heads is blustery and kind; he galumphs through the bedroom with a bird on his shoulder, a skunk at his heels. He is funny, wily, resourceful. He escapes the ship and puts the fire out; he befriends his captors and they dance together under the moon. Why not make Morton a woman, I ask her. She gurgles in assent. Let's make him a girl! Or why not make him not-human altogether? Let's make him a worldview, a spirit, a breath of untainted air, an extended hand. Let's make him the frond of a weeping willow, following the wind. Let's make him awe. Let's make him quiet. Let's make him love.

Twenty-two months since the Global Seed Vault was flooded by melting permafrost in the Arctic Circle

The baby begins to cry. She's recently been fed and changed, so maybe she's done with this story for now and wants to be held. I get up from the bed, cradle her head in my left hand and lay her over my right shoulder. We pick up the looping pilgrimage we began two days after she was born, walking from one end of the apartment to the other. I move slowly so she can study all the things I've long stopped noticing – the old photographs, the books with their multi-coloured spines, the stained-glass lamp with its bulb on a dimmer. We stop for a spell, easing the bulb from low to high, high to low, low to high.

Ten hours and fifty-three minutes from sunrise to sunset in late winter New York

We move from the lamp to the bedroom to the bedroom window, so we can look over 90th street from the second floor. It is a grey day, windy and damp enough to pretend we are standing on the deck of a ship, moored to this street, ready to set off across the sea. I place a white tissue in the baby's hand and we wave together, 'Bon voyage! Goodbye! Fare thee well, neighbours!' Her face is serious, expectant of the journey ahead. She clutches the tissue and awaits a reply, but the people below don't notice us. They look down, mesmerised by the screens cradled in their palms, deafened by their earbuds.

Twenty thousand years for the carbon emitted from a transatlantic flight to leave the atmosphere

Remember the moon? Let's go back. On 22nd December 2018, I stop on a sidewalk in New York City to look at the moon. It is a full moon, large in the sky, yet to stare it straight in the face I have to stand in a specific spot, hold my head very still, and aim my gaze between the silhouettes of buildings.

At this point the baby is three days late, and I believe this moon might draw her out. Pedestrians swerve around me without slowing their pace. I stare at the moon and the moon at me, as though sharing a secret across a crowded room. This patient observer of life on Earth, of human history. This baby, curled in a ball of animal muscle and light fur, genetically identical to the first *Homo sapiens* who roamed the Earth 200,000 years ago. She will be born a nomad, ready to pick berries and give meaning to the moon, or she will be born a modern consumer, ready to hunch shoulders over an iPhone and travel across the world in a single day. The buildings across the street flicker with the lights of fifty flat-screen TVs in the living rooms of identical apartments, each lulling its individual owner away from his neighbours, away from the moon.

Had Morton made it off that ship, the Morton of our fantasy, would my view be unobstructed, all these years later? Had Morton turned to wind and blown the colony away, would my neighbours be gathered together? Had the wind resurrected the maypole, would they still be squirrelled in separate boxes, watching separate televisions, spooning food from individual take-out containers, scrolling privately for inside jokes?

Twenty-two hours between the full moon and the birth of my daughter

I desperately want to show my daughter the world, yet I despair at what's become of it, what will have become of it, by the time she understands how much we've lost and for what. I question my morality for bringing her here even as I see her smile for the first time. I keep myself from thinking too deeply when I wrap her in blankets thoughtlessly decorated with cheerful images of all the animals that will be extinct when she is old enough to wonder about them.

When I'm 50, my daughter will be ten, and she will know. I stare at her face and already can't imagine life without her, yet the horror of what I've brought her into persists. And despite my greatest efforts to remain optimistic, I hope upon hope she will be stronger than I was, and will not want children.

THE END

No. Not like this. Let's try again.

Centuries ago, before the days of Morton and Endicott, parts of what is now Manhattan island were navigable by canoe. The Lenape people paddled the land, caught fish and gathered oysters from the clear waters, travelled quietly from the Hudson to the east, breathed clean air and listened to the sounds of birds, the songs of wind blowing through trees that lined the river banks.

Today my daughter and I stand amidst the blinking chain of knock-off electronics and plastic tchotchke shops on Canal Street, and it is impossible to imagine what the Lenape must have seen. Impossible for me. But she is new to this world, her imagination not yet calcified by expectation, disappointment and fear. Although mine are the feet that touch the ground and hers are suspended above it, I imagine she is the one who feels most acutely the pulse of those ancient streams, their history, their promise, their patience. They are buried, long since polluted, filled and paved over, but still they flow.

What is human history but a series of decisions, made by a series of people?

It is heartbreaking to think things could have gone a very different way. But these waters are patient. This wild is patient. I look down at my daughter, bundled to my chest, and despite the noise of the street she is facing out; her eyes are open. Her gaze passes the cars, the jackhammers, the keychains and handbags. Her gaze digs through the concrete and over the tops of high-rise buildings. Her gaze reaches the moon. Her gaze reaches the water.

What will the future be, but a series of decisions, made by a series of people?

When I'm 50, my daughter will be ten, and old enough to know. I stare at her face and already can't imagine life without her, yet the reality of what I've brought her into persists. And despite my greatest inclinations to remain pessimistic, I hope upon hope she will be stronger than I was and will remember those waters, and someday she and her children will swim and lie along the banks.

Mat Osmond

Black Madonna, Casa Alamosa Shrine

Living and speaking water is within me,
saying deep inside me, Home to the Father
– Origen, 6th Century C.E.

I'm that lizard-like thing
under Meinrad's feet
lifting its face to drink

as she bends her head
to an empty page
dreaming a flood of eels

and I'm all the world's reptiles
sipping her dark red words

God Is Not
God Is Not

God Is Not
A Boy's Name

which we already knew
but still

the eels slide off the page
they sing to the dry river bed

yes eels pour down from her page
writhe on the desert floor

where the world is dogs
at mid-day rest
a quiet girl on a stool

Serious spectacled girl
playing Artemis
playing Crow

we'll swallow your rose-red words
until we learn the rules

Rules are simple enough
she says

    Rules Are Flower
    Rules Are Song

Simple enough to forget
she says

which is how we get them wrong
But the world is three old dogs at rest
Meinrad, on a stool

and us
in the liquid carmine glow
of the Black Madonna's song

Note
'Black Madonna, Casa Alamosa Shrine' is one in a series of ekphrastic poems that reply to paintings of the same name by the American artist, writer and Benedictine nun Meinrad Craighead (d. 8th April 2019).

KATE WALTERS The Saint and the Oystercatcher

Book page and pen

This work was made during one of three artist residencies I had on the Isle of Iona. I was researching St. Brigid and the oystercatcher which came to protect her. I was also beginning to practise a process of tuning into my body in a deep way, and using it to help me sense things around me, in the great beauty and clarity of Iona.

Alastair McIntosh

God Carry Me

It was one of those strange conversations that happen during winter on the islands of the Scottish Hebrides. In the past, looking back beyond the 18th century, winter was when the bardic schools gathered. Taking advantage of the loss of outer light, they would deepen to the inner light, to scry into and speak unto the condition of the people.

We were coming down a rocky little gully in the west. She was of the Iona Community, one of many who, each year, conduct the plainsong daily chores that help sustain the ancient abbey. And she had been worn smooth from all the season's labours. A senior figure, mid-fifties, ordained in one of the mainline churches, she had known both sheer exhaustion in her job and perhaps what the military call 'the loneliness of high command'. The loneliness of what it means to see a complex situation from vantage points unavailable to others.

'Our calling', as one of her predecessors had once told me, 'is to carry a burden of awareness. But to come to know it as a *precious* burden of awareness.' Such a calling to vocation is – as the word suggests – vocal. Whether from outwith or within, it is something that is heard to be understood. And this is the challenging bit: it is something that it may not be our shout to call.

Think about the source of calling in our lives. Pink Floyd lyricised it thus: 'An echo of a distant time / Comes willowing across the sand.' Donovan, too, in the title of his 1968 album, 'Like It Is, Was, and Evermore Shall Be'. Hailing from Glasgow, he may have known the origin in Psalm 133, and in its gritty old Scots version: 'As it wes in the beginnin', is nou, an' aye sall laist.' Who would have believed that even back then, they were into definitions of 'sustainable development'?

I too am concerned with sustainability, with the depth that is called on us in these times, so that for as long as the Earth in its own rhythms and ways endures, 'aye sall laist.'

*

The Very Reverend Dr. George MacLeod, who founded the Iona Community in the 1930s, was a pioneering figure in green politics. In 1989, by which time he was into his nineties, he became the first peer to represent the Green Party in the House of Lords.

The first time that I met him had been almost a decade earlier. I was queuing for a railway ticket at Waverley Station in Edinburgh. There were about six lines, each with a dozen or more people waiting, and immediately in front of me stood a man of commanding frame and presence.

On hearing his aristocratic accent – family circumstance had led him to possess the articulation of the English landed classes rather than a clergyman of Highland provenance – I peered around his shoulder. The chequebook that he held announced: *Lord MacLeod of Fuinary*.

'Excuse me,' I said, touching a hand on his shoulder as the clerk processed his ticket. 'Would you be Lord MacLeod, the anti-nuclear man?' He was, at that time, battering the Church of Scotland at its General Assembly each year, eventually succeeding in getting them to declare nuclear weapons ungodly.

He turned a full 180 degrees, to face me directly, before delivering his answer. 'I most certainly am Lord MacLeod, the anti-nuclear man,' he boomed, right across the station.

Work stopped at every kiosk. Everybody turned and froze, their attention galvanised, as if onto a pop-up pulpit.

'And have you heard the latest news?'

'What is that?' I asked, self-consciously.

'The Americans have just named their latest nuclear submarine *Corpus Christi*. The Body of Christ. Now, *that is blasphemy!*'

He turned back round, and carried on writing out his cheque.

Twice decorated for bravery in the Great War, George's emergent pacifism was all the more cogent because he had engaged first-hand in death. 'How does it feel to be returning once more to Iona?' a journalist had once asked him on the pier at Fionnphort, hoping for a jubilant feel-good response.

He answered grimly: 'It feels like getting back into the trenches.' George knew the cost of battle, both materially and spiritually.

He was not alone with such experiences on Iona. Around the year AD 698, Saint Adomnán, the eighth abbot after Saint Columba, mentioned that a book he had just finished had been written 'in what I admit is a poor style, but I have done so in the face of daily labour coming from all sides: the sheer volume of ecclesiastical concerns seems so overwhelming.'

Columba himself, Adomnán tells us, 'often brought spiritual refreshment to certain of his monks who felt that he came in spirit to meet them on the road.'

They'd reach the halfway point across the island after spending all day at the harvest, when 'each of them seemed to feel a wonderful and strange sensation.' As one described it:

> In the last few days and even now, I am conscious of a wonderful fragrance like all flowers gathered into one; and of heat like fire, not the fire of torment but somehow sweet. And I feel too a strange, incomparable joy poured into my heart. In an instant it refreshes me wonderfully and makes me so joyful that I forget all sadness, all toil. Even the load on my back, though it is not light, none the less from this point all the way to the monastery – I know not how – feels weightless so that I cannot tell I am carrying it. (Adomnán, *Vita*, 1:37).

*

So there we were. She of the modern-day Iona Community, and me, in the second decade of this Third Millennium. She had led us in a pilgrim group down to Saint Columba's Bay. Now, we were heading back, picking a way down through a fissure between the rocks that opens to the broad Atlantic beach. From there, there is nothing until Newfoundland. We had slipped back from the rest, just out of earshot.

'So how's it been?' I asked her.

'It's been better this year,' she confided, 'but at its worst, angels carried me.'

'Angels?' I said, a little nonplussed (but only a little – it's not uncommon in the Hebrides to hear such stories).

'Yes, angels of a sort,' she smiled.

'It was very simple, really,' she continued. 'Disarmingly so. I was coming down this little valley, weighed down by the burdens of the year, struggling with how to carry on with each next step.'

'I was coming down, just as we are now, a little apart from the rest of the group, when I became aware that George MacLeod and Saint Columba were at my side. And they were carrying me.'

*

She and I hadn't been in contact for some years. In the writing of this essay, I enquired to find a recent email address and dropped her a line. Might I use her story? Had I remembered it correctly? She answered warmly in the affirmative, adding:

> That descent of the brae has stayed with me as a moment of such deep reassurance – those two great men gently and powerfully came either side of me and carried me down the brae. And so I carried on.

*

I am not asking you to believe that Saint Columba literally reappeared, in person, with his good pal George Macleod, to aid my friend through times of trouble. That would be to misplace focus onto the small question. It would be to frame a greater truth inside a limited understanding of space and time and consciousness such as can only handle smaller truths. It would be to try to trump the mythos – the inner imaginal realm (which is not the same as make-believe imaginary) that sustains the meanings of reality – with the realm of the logos, the outer reasoning powers, by which we order and interrogate the world.

In an essay called 'The Religion of the Future', the late Indian-Spanish and Hindu-Christian scholar, Raimon Panikkar, examines the difficulties that the modern Western mind faces in finding itself compelled to conduct 'an intense reading of the signs of the times'. The essence of the difficulty, he suggests, is that we approach the future by extrapolating from the present. However, 'not everything is fully contained in the present', and so, 'Ultimately, the answer to this question belongs to prophecy.' In particular, prophesy that addresses the pressing issues of our time, whether in the microcosm of a movement like the Iona Community, or the macrocosm of such 'wicked' global problems as poverty, war and ecocide, from the vantage point of mythos, as well as logos.

> [It] open[s] up a fundamental reflexion into contemporary man's self-understanding. What is going on here is a particular example of the inter-dependency between the *mythos* and the *logos*. The human *logos* can only function within a concrete *mythos*, but this *mythos* in turn is conditioned by the interpretation the *logos* gives to it. In our day, definitions of religion, most of them of Western mint, cannot avoid presenting the content as well as the function of religion, from within a given perspective basically conditioned by history. Therefore, if today the myth is undergoing a mutation, our fundamental understanding of religion must also undergo a modification. This is not so much a matter of 'new religions' of the future as of a new experience of the religious dimension of existence.

The daily problems with which the carriers of spiritual life on Iona had wrestled, from the monks of Columba's time, through Adomnán, all the way on to my friend and others like her today, were of the realm of logos; but their seeing through came from the depth of mythos.

The West has tended to speak of God in terms of logos – translated in John's gospel through a Greek perception plane as 'the Word'. The East counterpoints this with the mystery of mythos. These, like the Yin and the Yang both held within the wholeness of the Tao, are interdependent, as Panikkar points out. A Hindu term that expresses that underlying wholeness is the *dharma*. Dharma is often translated as the 'truth' or 'law', but literally the Sanskrit means 'that which sustains'. Stretched out through space and time, from out of all eternity, it is the ongoing opening of the way of God. In Christian teaching, 'I am the way, the truth and the life' (John 14:6) perfectly expresses this dynamic sense of dharma.

There is an intriguing overlap of both sound and meaning between the proto-Indo-European dher- as the root of 'dharma', and dhe- as the root of 'doom'. Sanskrit scholars tell me this is probably just coincidental. But in the mischievous etymologies of the mind, to conflate them serves to hint that in our doom is our dharma. When Private Frazer used to say 'We're a' doomed' in the British comedy, *Dad's Army*, he was speaking (as a Scotsman should) the deepest spiritual truth.

The mistake of some faith traditions is to approach doom too rationally, and to miss the insight of the mystics – both of East and West – that we are integral participants in the whole. Says the *Isa Upanishad*: 'Who sees all beings in his own Self, and his own Self in all beings, loses all fear.' Says the Second Letter of Peter, 1:4 in the King James translation: '... that by these ye might be partakers of the divine nature'.

It is not that we are handed down our doom, or that we have it dumped upon us by some higher authoritarian power. Rather, our doom or destiny read as opening to the dharma is the deep unfolding of our nature, our authenticity, our self-realisation – and note the Upanishad's remark that there is no fear in doom, so understood.

Uncivilisation, the Dark Mountain manifesto, speaks of doom in the way that folks involved in movements such as Extinction Rebellion do:

> Secretly, we all think we are doomed: even the politicians think this; even the environmentalists. Some of us deal with it by going shopping. Some deal with it by hoping it is true. Some give up in despair. Some work frantically to try and fend off the coming storm.

Am I in danger here of confusing categories of doom? Only if we fail to see that the relative doom of our daily lives is held within the greater hand of absolute doom – the dharma – that opening of the way of God. It is noteworthy that in Scotland there are 'doomster' hills, places where the laws as 'doom' were handed down. Here tribal right relationships, or dharma as it might be said, were set in place.

To survive spiritually in coming times, we have to operate within both space and time, with the practicalities of the logos. But we also have to operate outside of space and time, in the prophetic realm of visioning that is the mythos. We have to get on with both the daily grind on 'Iona' – or acting on the world's ecological plight, or whatever is our calling – *and* we have to learn to see the wider picture that sustains it all as we – with Blake – become the builders of 'Jerusalem', what Martin Luther

King spoke of as 'the beloved community'. Again, in our doom is our dharma.

'And so I carried on,' said my friend.

*

God carry me was the expression – the mantra or the prayer, one might say – that came to me when I reflected on this and similar experiences of struggle against the odds. These days, weighed down with demands, or when walking into situations that I'm not sure how to handle, I repeat those words: *God carry me*. Let go into the dharma – the way, the truth and the life.

*

But *how*? I hear the persistent question. *How* do we ground all that?

In 1990, after Raimon Panikkar had delivered his Gifford Lectures at the University of Edinburgh (now published as *The Rhythm of Being*), a small group of us, headed up by Alastair Hulbert, invited him to come to Govan, the hard-pressed former mercantile ship-building area of Glasgow. At the end of a scintillating lecture titled 'Agriculture, Technoculture, or Human Culture?' I asked him:

'Panikkarji, you have given a brilliant exposition of what is wrong with the world. But *how* can we…'

I hardly needed to finish. He replied, 'It is not for me to tell you the how. You must work out the how for yourself.'

I was left slightly unsatisfied. Afterwards, Professor Frank Whaling of Edinburgh University took him upstairs to conduct an interview. It fell on me to deliver a pot of tea.

I poured it out and offered milk. Panikkar reached out for the sugar. One spoon. Two spoons. Three heaped spoons.

He was about to dip into the bowl for a fourth time, when he paused, looked up at me, and realising that he'd just been talking about culture and cultural differences, asked, 'How many…?'

It came to me quick as a flash. 'Panikkarji! It is not for me to tell you the how. You must…'

The great soul, *mahatma,* that he was, roared with laughter. I can't remember if he took the extra spoonful, but the question never goes away. *How* can we birth – or rather, be birthed by – processes that are beyond our ken, into the deepening journey that gives life?

We cannot prescribe the *how*. Panikkarji was right in that. But we can accompany, witness and testify. It is for this reason that my wife and I are involved with the GalGael Trust in Govan, where we live. Outwardly our people build traditional wooden boats and, with them, connect to the natural environment. Inwardly, we hold open a space where people who have been through crushing times can rebuild their lives; by opening the doors of creativity, holding spaces for conviviality, and learning how to be community.

For each of the past four years, we have made a weekend pilgrimage to Iona – in March, before the tourists turn up. With the help of a Quaker trust and benefactors who appear by magic, we hire a couple of minibuses, John at the Iona Hostel gives a friendly rate, and we head up on a Friday morning by road and two ferries. There, we settle into a very loose exploration of what 'spirituality' may, or may not, mean for us. On the Saturday we'll visit the medieval abbey, the Celtic knotwork on the ancient stones a testament to our people's creativity. We'll take a pilgrimage down to Saint Columba's Bay. In the evening, we'll have a deep sharing around what gives folks meaning, perhaps down on the beach or in one of the abbey's side chapels. On the Sunday, we'll have a final sharing round the hostel table and then climb the hill and have a splash in the Well of Eternal Youth, before taking the ferry home.

In the outer sense of logos, it is about creating a container for experience. But what happens inwardly? One of our folk left us with a streetwise answer to the question *how?*

> Pain is the touchstone of spirituality. That's what speaks to me. In the darkest spaces of my life, I know there's somebody with me. I never went looking for that in Iona, but on Iona you could feel the life you were created for. I felt alive, looking at the stars, you could touch them. That, in a nutshell, is spirituality. If you don't go within, you go without.

Raquel Vasquez Gilliland

Excerpt from
Letter to the Ancestry Company

I want to know if my great-great-
great-grandmother's grandmother
liked the rain. If it reminded her
of something longer than blood.
If it made her feel like the earth
were calling an ancient lover.
If thunder made her shiver,
but the good kind of shiver, like when
a palm leaf brushes your shoulder
as you walk in the cold mud.
Did the rain clouds remind her
of the birth caul of her children,
did it seem like the sky was fertile
before each feral storm. If lightning
looked to her like cracks opening
to a new universe, one where rain
spoke backward and cried from time
to time. Did she name each sort of
heavy cloud. Were the huge ones
'underwood at dusk',
the accompanying wispy gray,
'baby hair'. Were her favourite
the clouds that arrive after
the storm, before the set sun,
when the whole world drips
with rose gold? 'Cause that's
my favourite. Can you tell me, please?
Did I get that from her?

REBECCA CLARK

Stafford's Deer

Graphite on paper

Stafford's Deer is based on the poem 'Traveling through the Dark' by American poet and pacifist William E. Stafford. I felt compelled to dignify the death of this beautiful creature in an imagined, isolated moment. Perhaps the act of drawing her was a form a penance. We are all travelling through the dark.

Martin Shaw

Looking for Wolf Milk

Winter gods lope the forest
Strike you with their wolfskin glove

And the counterfeit life
Takes its carrion demands
Back to the blue deceits
Of the one who first folded you.

I trust words like that more than therapy talk, or becoming-your-best-self, or some strangulated idea about enlightenment. I trust, too, that there is an owl that lands on your face as you gather sticks by the river and you fall into a trance for three days. Such an image both thrills and alarms as it can't be franchised or easily fetishised, because the mandate of suffering is so clearly part of the mix. And such an encounter could lead god knows where.

What follows is something of what I've experienced over almost 20 years as a wilderness rites of passage guide. I hope it provokes and excites and absolutely does not pretend the endeavour is anything less than highly mysterious. Natural, yes. But mysterious. What follows is a glimpse through the three stages of the process: severance, threshold, return.

We'll get to the return to the village later. When we get there I'll bang on about seemingly antiquated values: compassion, upstandingness, vocation, grace under pressure. That we actually raise our kids. That we live cleanly in our relationship to others. That our enchantments and befuddlements are limited in impact, that we don't pass them on. The village is essential for the distillation of epiphany into wisdom. Human contact. But I'm not there yet.

Right now I'm defending the strange and usefully dangerous elements of the vigil. The moments that may never sift into daylight illumination but are like a rook pecking on your liver down in the pure animal of your body. Peck peck peck. It's that pecking that keeps us restless. It's a good thing to be restless. It's the kind of thing that gets folks out on the hill in the first place.

To sit in a copse at dusk
Can be a kind of loneliness
As lights prick up the distant town

But to be amongst them
Can also be a
Fierce hit of sorrow

My bridge of words
To speak such things
Is tissue-thin
A sparrow's weight
Would fell it
But now and then
I find moon-flint.

Outside.

To be buffeted by weather, to have hands pink as the flesh of Galway salmon as you splash freezing water in your just-woken face. To be a million nerve endings reaching out to darkness, rain, and white-crack lightning storm. To sleep a-jumble in your clothes because of the freeze, spend weeks without seeing your reflection, with no devices that beep and glow anywhere near. To feel jubilant, grief-struck, maybe even wild.

For just a little while, I ask you to consider trading comfort for shelter. To ask: what does it mean to be dreamt rather than dream, to be claimed by a place rather than claim it? For some of us, these are yearnings almost painful to contemplate.

What does it look like?
Four days and nights alone in the forest.
Just like the fairy tales.

That's the brass tacks of it. The unadorned, above-ground synopsis. No tent, no fire, no food. Just a tarp, sleeping bag and some water. Let the land have at you.

The wilderness vigil is immeasurably ancient, and the way our ancestors tuned their ear to the living earth. This is always the place we have gone to mark transitions – from one stage of life to another. It can be difficult, wonderful, resolutely un-ecstatic, and absolutely life-changing. Tribal folk have always known it was where you go to die and get born. A place where big questions get asked, things bend their heads to die and green shoots spring up. Four days to maybe, just for a moment, behold Wild Land Dreaming.

This is not a teaching from a human realm. Important. No human guru. Only copse guru, stream guru, spirit guru. This is the regal old bones of the mountain as teacher, the swift raven overhead as guide. This is ancestor time. They can be tough instructors, but grip blessings in their beaks.

Leaving the village

The ragged call of night crow
Is my chanteuse, oh rogue, oh brigand
Of the wet black branch
Merrie I am merrie
As the heavenly farrier
Hooves my steed
Of ghoul and shadow
Merrie I am merrie
In my way
Oh ragged call of night crow

First move. There seems to be an understanding from the aboriginal cultures of the world that the forest makes you as much as the village does. When I say village and forest I mean settled, human community and the wild.

There is an appropriate untangling to take place at adolescence from roles that the community has already deposited on you. For modern folks, that means for a time you are not your job description, or a partner, or a parent. You are cracked loose from any societal crustacean covering your mischievous hide. Down the road a little, none of these attributes are necessarily a problem, but the emphasis in rites of passage is to be porous to the mysteries awhile. And most of us need quite a shakedown to get to that point.

So in the way I'm presenting it, you need to leave the steady life, the easy ticket, the done deal.

It's only then you may breathe deep enough to behold what the gods are trying to really disclose to you. And traditionally that's best encountered in a wild and lonely place. It doesn't tend to happen with the Range Rover ticking over, and a belly full of bacon and eggs. This leaving the village (or town, or city) is often called *Severance*.

> Jakob Boehme, the German mystic... liked to say that "In Yea and Nay all things consist." Liminality may perhaps be regarded as the Nay to all positive structural assertions, but in some sense the source of them all, and, more than that, as a realm of pure possibility whence novel configurations of ideas and relations many arise.
>
> – Victor Turner

This encapsulates much of where I want to go. Nebulous though it may seem, in a culture of health, structures are created not by resistance to the mysteries but openness to them. And the reverie in which we best open ourselves to the mysteries leads inevitably to participation, reverence, right action, a recalibration of the heart. I believe the mistake is when we unpack the uncanny too swiftly, or consciously disable it with interpretations that strip it of its divine eccentricity. We stuff the wild animal and mount it on the wall. Much subtlety of thought is needed between village and forest, especially with so much weighted in the village's favour.

Funny word, liminal. From the latin – *limen* – meaning threshold. It seems a little over-utilised these days, and it has no image secreted within it, so it easily slips away from anything I can grip. Then again, I wonder if that is the point. Its essential ambiguity.

Submission: austerities to fit our schedule

Some would argue that it sounds a little excessive, or doesn't require the stewarding of guides. I mean, isn't it just camping for a few days? I once saw an ad that said 'Vision Quests for Busy People', and appeared to offer a quick jog through the trouble in just a few hours. As usual, we reduce the austerities to fit our schedule. The god of us dictates the terms as usual. And in that very sentiment is the malfunction of many contemporary attempts at rites-of-passage. We don't like the word that resides at the very centre of the experience: *submission.*

We don't want to submit, we want to dictate. But if we don't submit then we never enter the burning ground of the encounter, and healing or anything even half like it simply can't enter. You came to the forest for something to die, and it can't die if you don't submit. If there's a rebirth in any of this, then you have to go down first. Otherwise it's a faux-initiation, and god knows they are in ready supply.

If you attempt a wilderness vigil alone, then the likelihood is you will go too hard or too soft on yourself. The parameters of the encounter will not be clear, and that's where real, un-useful danger is present. The porosity of the experience needs to be met by the solid edges of the guide, that's the correct alchemical reboot. There is such a thing as too much great spirit. The boundaries of the vigil are a large part of its effectiveness. The humbling of submitting to the experience is no bad thing.

It's a radical position, to enter a wild place and willingly go without food. To be a different kind of hunter, to leave more than you took, to make prayers not chainsaw cuts. Crucially, the wild place is not a backdrop to your individuation, at least not in any predictable, by-rote manner. Nor is it a fixative exactly, but it's likely going to reveal a more complex picture of your constellation *within* it. Likely it's going to burden you with that arrangement.

It's a holy thing, that burden. We are culturally drowning in ignorance of it. Your legs should totter a little underneath it.

Every stumble shows appropriate inheritance
That you found both great work and the requisite defeat
That paves its quiet and crooked path

Severance contains the real possibility of understanding that during your life thus far you have been fed counterfeit directives. Directives that serve others rather well, but your soul not a jot. Directives that are a kind of chloroform to your nature. That contort their societal shape over the natural, funky, wide-eyed blinking beasty character of your own. This awareness is not the same thing as rejecting discipline, not the same thing as resistance to all authority, but ensuring you have a fundament of mythic ground to work out of. Without that, invasion is likely. Not just of continent but of consciousness.

If you pick up any anthropological account of traditional rites of passage you quickly realise that they have more than a little invested in an encounter with the mysteries. You realise that the communication of the encounter tends to arrive without a soundbite. No bullet points for when you met the Banshee. The encounter heads for the body first, a bone-shaker rather than a brain-refiner. Articulation is something away aways. Right now you are a half-blown motor in the garage of the spirits as they stand around smoking and peering at you. Then surgery begins. The whole thing tends to be in language we don't have the words for.

It's easier, much more manageable, to place a psychological gloss on the process, but the prophetic, the uncanny and the spiritually unruly have a place in it. The difference is that back in the day, every single person you returned to had experienced something of the same rewiring.

Restore the girl
That glanced over the farmer's gate
And saw 10,000 Irish spears
Protruding from pale dew
The girl that saw a man too small for reality
Squatting halfway up a mountainside

We now enter the second stage, threshold.

Early in the morning the fasters are out. A little holy smoke blown in their face, no tea. They walk silently to their spots. They are in the House of the Spirits for the next four days. We will tend fire, send prayers daily, cluck with worry, but they are in the Otherworld now. That's absolutely how we experience it. There's no knowing wink as they leave. It's not an elaborate theatre. What happens now is up to the Ones That Stand Behind Us.

Waking the bone pile

As they leave we see Gawain stealing his way to the Green Chapel, Persephone heading to the Underworld, Odysseus trying to get home to Ithaca. No matter how urbane the participants may appear, myths hang on their shoulders like a half-remembered but utterly vital cloak. They have entered myth-time, and everything that now shows up is some sideways form of illumination towards the idiosyncratic turns of their own story.

There is almost always a bone pile waiting out there in the bush for the participant. The more attention you give it, the bigger it tends to get. Bone piles are all the little deaths that have occurred during your life. The crossroads moments where something or someone got chucked under the truck. Grieved or un-grieved, they are there. The vigil is often a tending to that. A tending, but also a questioning: what in me got sent into exile?

A wilderness vigil means no distance left to run. It means sitting down and eyeballing the big sullen lump of splinter-bone and moss. It means attending to your dead. You can talk to them, dance for them, weep for them, pray for them, cradle them in silk and soak their bones in wine, curate all the appropriate sorrows and fierce remembering they require. Be a human being for Christ's sake.

What happens? It means a resurrection of energy and focus, a calling home of things abandoned. It is a needed re-animation, a possibly unenviable ceremony of remembrance and accountability, an essential regrouping of the soul. You don't need bells and smells to do this, you don't need to be some high-end magician, you simply need to show up and keep showing up. The fast itself is the most grandiloquent container for such labour.

I think you can follow what I'm saying. Here's it condensed: whilst alone in the woods you will inevitably be led to reflect on the difficulties of your life. To do so in such a charged experience can work as a restorative; and you holistically start to re-inhabit parts of yourself you may have become numb to or distanced from. In this way you wake the bone pile.

It says four days but I wonder again if it's false advertising. Maybe we should fess up and say four years.

The last night of the fast you stand up in your circle, praying and facing the darkness. Maybe you'll catch the scent of Baba Yaga. Yaga is really too dangerous to talk about, so I'm being careful. She is a primal and sophisticated initiator of scary, turbulent, educational descent. She'll kill you so you live better. She's a Queen of the Beneath.

Some say she is the embodiment of a terrible winter storm, her broom sweeping the blizzard away as she hurtles through the darkness, a suffocating, nightmarish presence. At least when she feels like it. In the eighteenth century, the writer Matthew Guthrie made associations of Yaga with Persephone, and Mikhail Chulkov identified her as a Slavic goddess, worthy of blood sacrifice and with breasts that lactate rain. She will nip the teeth from children as they sleep, and replace them with little stumps of iron, screwed into their gums.

But she also curates morality in humans, oversees women who spin and weave, is even a midwife at the beginning and end of life. And there's this notion that she originated as a storm cloud, life-giving in the summer months, life-taking in the winter. Let's hold onto that image, and the essential ambiguity it raises. To know Yaga is to learn to speak from both sides of your mouth, to have chewed on smelly bones as well as snorted the perfume of Aphrodite. Check your wisdom teeth, there may be a little iron back there.

There's a very particular kind of life force that comes through encounters with her. A life force that is nothing to do with kale and obsessive stretching and thinking unpolluted thoughts. Yaga can make you think things you never thought before: you pull the morphine drip from your mouth and break from an anaesthetised world. You look like you've been dragged through a hedge backwards, but fuck it, you're alive. She can even put you in touch with your desire.

So what is happening mythically to the midnight shuffler? The vigil participant? They are dancing with Grendel, entering that Chapel Perilous, negotiating with Yaga. In the oldest way imaginable they are truly turning up for their own life. Something in them demanded such wolf milk.

And now the Return.

After the elation of completing and the sweetness of being reunited with fellow fasters, profound exhaustion kicks in. Most crawl into their tents for a few hours sleep. And the Ritz-Carlton that little tent is after their rain-addled tarp. As they sleep or review their journal, we stoke the fire, gather stools and stumps of trees in a circle and light the lanterns. Soon it'll be time for the stories.

Village speech tends to betray us
Words curl from jaw then can go no further
The clatter of the wagons surround the coyote
As we try and push the winged words out

As the daylight starts to dip a little, they begin to speak. A common phenomenon is that in their proximity to the event and their exhaustion, they report that very little happened. Their faces are no longer fresh and open like their dawn return, but grey and tense in the public circle. Will their disclosure cut it?

Have they failed?

They almost always think they have.

Forest speaks through human

Over the last few years, I've come to the thinking that mirroring is most effective when the guide hears the sound of the forest speaking through the faster. When the place itself reports back through the faltering succession of recountings. That's what I listen for now. Not a hastily prepared model of healing to appeal to the intellect, but those strange, knotted sets of circumstance that indicate to a trained ear that some kind of real contact was established. So as they speak, I'm only partially listening to them. What I'm really listening out for is their *place* speaking back to me. That's the conversation I'm most invested in, and it happens. Not always, but often.

The real work is about to begin. In many ways the vigil is over and the quest has just begun.

There are no guarantees whatsoever that the vigil will grow fruit on the return. An enormous amount of that is down to the character and sheer devotion of the participant. It is easier to put the thing on the shelf with other esoteric holidays one has taken. But most of what happened out there happened underneath. You may not have received a roadmap but an atmosphere, an atmosphere to work out of. I know I didn't receive any kind of map, rather an un-mapping.

To go from an initiate to a quester is an endeavour to make the experience coherent and useful to others. It's an old bardic road, to get jabbered at by the holy natural forces of the world, then communicate something of that in a translatable, human form. But with a world on fire, what could be more important than listening to the earth speak in myth? That's what I think goes on in the vigil. You are slowly ground and simmered into old patternings of beholding which may seem almost worthless because the tributaries are now so culturally overgrown. That's an acute challenge. How far do you go into the language of today to communicate the murmurs of place without losing their nuance altogether?

The society you will return to is most likely not hopping from foot to foot in anticipation of your hard-won insight. Don't splurge the experience. Sit on it for a year, let it gestate, let it mature. Really think through the truest and most adroit form of expression. Be original. Don't compromise. Don't pull the stinger out, don't pull out the teeth.

It is your task to walk back from the vigil with an *animal*, not a pelt, not a corpse, but something alive. Curate that energy, feed it, don't domesticate it, make culture from it. It should be walking alongside you, not slung over your shoulder. You build your structures from its growls.

The rub is that the hardest part has just begun. The real testing ground. The clearest insight I've had about wilderness rites of passage is that the vulnerability of the return far outweighs what waits in the bush. That may not be the case in other countries but it's accurate in England. Sure, keep an eye for a tic and the belling stag, but for sustaining and developing the belly-dark insights of the ordeal only *now* are you are entering the perilous.

This is where I make some Trickster suggestions: to *not* go home, to walk a crooked walk, to see with the eyes of an elk. Return as smoke not as Moses. You can enjoy thinking about what that could look like.

Wilderness epiphany matures into village wisdoms

The wingspan of this essay is occulted experience and profound humanity. One does not exclude the other, but makes for a life worth gossiping about. Reverence opens to humanity.

The towns we sometimes sneer at have quiet and nourishing love affairs of 50 years' standing, acts of decency and courage frequently colluding, neighbourhoods that tough stuff out, sometimes flourish. Many of us come from some place like that. I said before that the visions of the forest didn't make me wise. It's true. They didn't. Reverent yes. The nearest I've ever got to wisdom is carrying that reverence back into such towns and trying to keep a doorway open to the wild. That very tension is what makes the cord stay good and tight in you, not slack with either amnesia or escapism. It's called counterweight.

Maybe your mother is back there somewhere, lonely for you. Maybe there is a debt needing to be repaid.

There could be a mess to clean up in some area of your life. Make a call, show up. Pretending to be badger, a trapper from the 1800's, or the Jackson Pollock of the northern wastes is all very fine, but not if you are on the run from your own morality. You're not a salmon, a thrush, or a boar. You are a guy called Joseph and you need to get your crap in a pile.

Despite all the emphasis on mystery I give, if it's functioning right it will crack open our husk of indifference too. Your heart will be exposed. But you can't hide out in the bush forever. The call to action is now. It is. We can't be naive about that. But if we don't get into nature we can't hear a damn word the earth is saying.

I promise you, you can live in the tension between the forest and the hum, thrum and clatter-drum of the village. You can. Don't go numb. Decide to keep remembering. That's what storytelling is, a decision to keep remembering. Not the low-grade stuff, but the real thing. The redemptive, the grace. Let's stop being afraid of words like that.

Bring your hands
Like proud cattle of the field
To the things that culture
Most needs you to till

What I want to do here is make a concerted plea here for you to become a story carrier. I say this as seriously as I would speak of the labour of becoming a shield-maiden for Boudicca, or being on one knee in front of Arthur, or sitting in the longhouse as the snow falls and the people brood on how to survive another winter. As seriously as you working for Greenpeace or becoming a professor of gender studies. I say this in the midst of Western amnesia and the glorious chloroform of privilege. I say this because knowing how to carry your story, being freighted in your story can not only save your own life for the days you are to have, but it can bring life to others too.

If there are too many horns blowing, and snorting of Castilian steeds in that statement, then so be it. I do not retreat, I do not step back.

The Return involves articulation of a *communicable* gift to others and the grounding of study, as well as the experiential provides a roundedness to our articulation. We are moving from a leap to a bridge. The leap is great for us, but the bridge has more utility for others. Pablo Neruda has that kind of generosity in his poems – a shared recognition, rather than a language so gnostic only he can enjoy it. So in honour of Neruda and all other nimble communicators between village and forest, I leave you with these words.

I lost my hat
On the way home
From the fair

I have a bright mind
Not a carrion mind

I stood under
The lime-green moon
In a time of dark reckoning

I stood until I had become a mystery
I stood until my inside was outside
I stood till I was less of myself

Underneath my cloak
There is a hare
Who is telling me things

References

Johns, Andreas, *Baba Yaga: The Ambiguous Mother and Witch of the Russian Folktale,* Peter Lang, 2004
Turner, Victor, *The Forest Of Symbols: Aspects of Ndembu Ritual,* Cornell University Press, 1967

Nancy Campbell

One Bear – Two Seals – The Knife

> 'It is through stories that we weave reality.'
> – *Uncivilisation*: *The Dark Mountain Manifesto*

Night time. I am working late – as usual – while bats flicker along the sandstone wall that divides the terrace from the river. There are pedestals on the wall at intervals, topped with weathered sculptures of people in ancient dress. Sometimes, especially at dusk, I catch these ancestors out of the corner of my eye and I forget they are made of stone – the stillness of the regiment, their proximity to my windows, unnerves me. Their eyes gaze across the river, towards the houses on the opposite bank where a few windows are lit.

It has been raining heavily today, and the river has a briny smell. I can hear the water rushing over the weir – and a more reluctant stream of musical notes from the studio of my neighbour, a composer who disrupts the strings of grand pianos and violins with elastic bands and fishing reels. In quiet moments, I hear my fingers as they scuffle across the keypad. Slowly, these sounds I am making will become a text, as the composer's will resolve into a score. I am thinking about the news this month – more than one million species are in danger says the latest report – nature is declining and extinction accelerating. The papers say it is a call to action, but not much action has been taken.

In some cultures, the names of the dead must not be spoken. How should I write, now? How to handle a noun once the object it refers to becomes extinct? Tenses turn from future to past, skipping the present. Prepositions grow obsolete. The page fills with nothing, or remains blank.

To wake my screen takes only a light and instinctive finger tap. That, at least, is speciously easy. But my laptop's hardware is a

One Bear – The Bear's Den – An Elk – Two Little Elks Lying – The Dog – The Mink – The Mink's House – A Small Owl – A Second Owl – Mallard Ducks – A Canoe – Two Men Fighting – Paddling Under Coppermaker – Wrinkled Face in the House – Unfolded

mystery to me. Rare earth minerals have been mined for it – and buried deep within by a distant labour force. It requires endless electrical power. In the apartment on the other side of mine, a writer is working on a novel. We're all so nocturnal here. The irregular clatter of her typewriter keys on the carriage bursts through the wall, a background percussion. Would it be better to write on a typewriter? Or should I look back to even older technology? Not far away from here, downriver, is the city of Mainz where in the 15th century Johannes Gutenberg – variously described as a blacksmith, goldsmith, manufacturer of mirrors, and publisher – invented a means for mass-producing moveable metal type, and combined this with other ingenious devices to print his 42-line Bible in 1455. From then on, ways of telling stories in Europe were never the same. Books were produced faster, more uniformly and in major editions for dissemination to ever more readers. Reality began to be woven differently.

*

These days, most publishers use digital methods of production, but there are still letterpress workshops engaged in hot-metal typesetting and hand printing. I've spent at least half my life working in them. I am not the only writer to fall for the striking visuals of letterpress, nor alone in admiring this technology for its more modest consumption of the Earth's resources. A decade ago, a pamphlet was published which urged storytellers and culturemakers to create alternatives to the fast, the uniform, the mainstream. The cover of *Uncivilisation: The Dark Mountain Manifesto* was letterpress-printed by Christian Brett of Bracketpress in Lancashire. The 'uncivilised writing' which the manifesto called for took the form of the journal which you hold in your hands. This journal continues to be designed and typeset at Bracketpress, the physical form of these books as significant as the content. This writing is 'Human, inhuman, stoic and entirely natural. Humble, questioning, suspicious of the big idea and the easy answer.'

– What's the Cry of the Geese? – The Walking Goose – A Toad – A Kick in the Back – Two Kelps (and Two Men Standing at the Ends of Them) – A Hummingbird – The Sparrow – Bird Invited by the Sparrow – Putting on the Belt – Invited a Second Time – The Log – Two Hummingbirds – Two Sitting on the Roof – Two Bears Seen by the Two on the Roof – Snot of a Woman – A Deer

There is no easy answer. Different stories need to be told now, and new technologies must be found to tell them. For stories are data, and data is greedy. Data storage has also been in the news. By 2025, the internet will consume a fifth of the world's electricity. The act of storytelling is never neutral, and the materials used may be complicit. The alphabet abets the end.

As ever more studies suggest that the grand human narrative is reaching its denouement, the potential for reproducing narratives are astonishing. The seemingly limitless dimensions of the internet vie with the conventional codex – a form that is finite in both page length and in edition size. Yet this line of text I construct, letter by letter, still owes much to Gutenberg. Here, in his shadow, I begin to renounce it. I look for an alternative way to tell the story of species extinction. And the alternative I find is string.

*

With a string, your hands could tie a knot, and this knot might look like many other things. With two hands and a knotted string you can make a circle or a square. For a thousand years or more, this circle or square was the screen on which string figures shifted, accompanied by chants or spoken stories.

The first string figure I encounter is that of the candle thief, a man who steals light from his neighbour. By coincidence, the candle thief is found in both Scotland, where I grew up, and Germany, where I am living now. When people travelled, as I have done, sharing ideas, trading stories, the string figures went with them, and now they are scattered around the world. This gallivanting candle thief would be a good familiar for one who writes at night. But the idea of darkness recalls the string traditions of other places I've lived – the Pacific Northwest and Greenland.

There are few studies of string figures; only hard-to-find volumes published in the last century. Diamond Jenness, who explored the Arctic around Coronation Gulf in Nunavut, published some findings in his *Report of the Canadian Arctic Expedition 1913–18*. The

Soviet ethnologist Julia Averkieva travelled to Vancouver Island with her supervisor Franz Boas in 1930 to record the string figures of the Kwakwa̲ka̲'wakw people. Averkieva's notes, which remained unpublished through both her long and distinguished career as an ethnologist and during her time in a labour camp, were recovered, edited and published by Mark A. Sherman, as *Kwakiutl String Figures*.

Not more than three generations before, Georges Cuvier, working at the National Museum in Paris, had developed his theory of catastrophes; his paper *Mémoires sur les espèces d'éléphants vivants et fossils* (1800) made the case for extinction. Before this, the consensus of science was that no species could die out. Fossils of extinct species had been discovered – the remains might not have looked like known creatures, but either the forms were so crumpled and incomplete they could be roughly ascribed to existing animals, or it was assumed they represented living animals yet to be encountered by biologists. The concept of extinction had to be created in the human mind, and it was created not long ago. Cuvier was only as far in time from Averkieva, as Averkieva is from me.

*

Some of the string figures Averkieva recorded represent animals; some showed everyday activities such as digging clams, or men fighting; others, objects of everyday use and natural phenomena: kelp, mountains, canoes, fire drills, spirits. Averkieva observed young men on Vancouver Island gathering in groups and spending their evenings 'going from house to house, strings in hand, competing with each other and with their hosts in the facility with which they executed and varied the designs of their figures.' The spiritual beliefs behind these games had faded, but the forms persisted as a test of skill and a method for memory training. The narratives might be violent or dream-like, the content familiar. The winner often blew his string in the face of his opponent, contemptuously bringing the contest to an end.

Jenness and Averkieva had a shared approach to transcription: their texts list the combination of finger and hand movements required – although the terms for each movement were argued over by different schools – followed by a line drawing of the finished figure. This breakdown was the best publishing could offer in the 20th century. But the instructions are complex and hard to follow; the diagram is hard to read. I stare at the angular, almost abstract forms. The crossing threads are tangled around each other like dogs' traces after they have been running for miles. Like a fossil. Even if I follow the instructions, I am not sure my loop of string would look like this, or be recognisable as the object it represents.

Learning to read the string takes time. I struggle to see in these figures the skeleton of the objects they represent. Sometimes the visuals are ambiguous, even on completion. In these shapeshifting signs, a bear can be a man. Those triangles could be mountains, or the prow of a canoe. The eye is trained to see multiplicity. It is best to be coaxed along by a player who can explain the tale.

*

Online I find a video of David 'Kitaq' Nicolai performing in Anchorage in 2010. He demonstrates one of the most difficult string figures, 'The Fox and the Whale'. While talking to the audience, his fingers scumble together a series of knots in seconds. Then he shakes his work out again. 'The thing about string figures, you always have to show up at the end with a clean loop.' The evidence disappears in a moment. A piece of string can be erased and reformed, over and over. When you pull it apart, it unravels so swiftly.

Sometimes the process of making is integral to the story – as in 'The Whale Floats up to the Surface of the Water' – but most often the focus is the shape in the hands at the end.

I begin to write about the figures but cast off these texts again before they are complete, shake them out like a loop of string. My process seems resistant, even in details: every time I type 'string' my

Fire Drill – Walking Sticks of an Old Woman – A Ship with Two Masts – A Ship with Opened Sails – Sneezing – Mountains with Clouds Between Them – A Mountain Broken in Two – It Sits Down and a Man Ahead of it – Man Tying the Rope Around his Neck in the Woods – Man Hanging by his Neck – A Porcupine – Two Brothers-in-Law Meeting – The Fish Trap – Two Killer Whales – Another

finger slips and it comes out as 'strong'. I can't touch type. I wonder about writing, about the point of writing, about all the hundreds of words I am trying to string together. The texts I am writing – if they were in string, how unwieldy they'd be.

String is inclusive. The figures might be made from plant fibres, a strand of yarn, a thong or sinew, a plait of hair. The sinister spirit of string figures – a warning to children – was said to pull out its own intestines to play with. Averkieva used a shoelace, you can see it in her photographs.

I close my laptop, light a candle and pick up a ball of string.

*

How long is a piece of string? Surely a long one when you need to create a whale, a short one when you need to create a flea? But no, scale is equivocal, and the flea may be as big as, or bigger than, a whale. The string should always be as long as a whip. Many wear it looped around their neck before they begin to play.

There were rules. Jenness was told that string games should only be played in the dark, due to a legend 'that the sun once beheld a man playing cat's cradles and tickled him.' Anyone who made figures before the sun had set might be accused of bringing bad weather. In Hudson Bay, others encountered different beliefs: 'According to Captain Comer the natives of Iglulik play cat's cradles in the fall when the sun is going south, to catch it in the meshes of the string and so prevent its disappearance.' A powerful string would stop the season shifting.

A large circle, doubled, trebled so my hands are contained within the string. I poke the tip of my left index finger under a loop, hook it around another finger. Pause. My hands move together and apart – and then draw inwards again, making a series of symmetrical movements, one finger, then the next, like rowing – I become a web of human and string, tying myself to invisible ideas. The string is no longer a string – it becomes another thing in every maker's mind.

Sweetheart – Not Passing Through – Passing Through – Trick on the Speed of Making It – Cheek of the Halibut – Moving the Loops – A Catch – A Fly on the Nose – Cutting off the Fingers – Cutting off the Wrist – Catching a Leg – Threading a Closed Loop – Making a False Knot – The Knife –

*

The knot travels around and along. The string tightens, and digs into the crook of my thumb. Gradually my hands pull closer. I have imprisoned myself in my own story. The figures are companionable, balanced, a mirror reflecting the work of two hands. The twisted patterns will be more or less the same among all players but the size and shape depend on the character of those hands – the thickness and angle of fingers.

Sometimes the figures are drawn from the string, sometimes from the spaces between. But the story always relies on these spaces. The fingers hold the string apart, outlining sections of air. The strings cross each other but the fingers never meet. Hands turn over, turn inside out, and then upend the arrangement, peeling it backwards. Discarded, it falls in tangles to the ground, in a new pattern. Unplanned, untethered. This is the game about nothing: to create something of nothing and make it disappear again. A knife of course, can cut a string – unless it is a knife of string.

String is a web for a land without spiders. The net you throw over something to catch it. A string is both circular and linear, the best way to tell a story with no beginning or ending. With no known ending or beginning. Looped around the wrists by night, by day it cuts a line across the snow – across the sea – a harbour wall – a harpoon line – a coastline – the limit of sea ice or water level. String will secure things – lash wood to wood or bone to bone. It stops things being stolen – stops ropes unravelling – stops containers opening of their own accord – plays its part in tethering creatures. It ties one thing and another, ties here to there. It dances around its own tension. With a good knot, it will never fray. It is what draws the flensed skin taut on the frame – always the middleman, between or around things. What was the last thing you used a string for?

The sun begins to rise. The hands are most dextrous, when they are tied.

Em Strang

Tog Muhoni

Because when you see him you know (small light in a night forest),
that his name is Tog Muhoni and his smile tells the way the river bends
and how he crossed it, one foot dragging behind like a snapped limb:
to stay or to go? You're late for something, driving, and your whole life
is mapped out in the arm he's missing. The shoulder blade is intact,
you can see as you slow down, rub the breath from the windscreen
and stare in the way your mother would have scolded. An owl
inside your head this morning, eyes, silent inquisition:
his body seems to shift, migrate from one shape to another
or he's just a ghost waving in the cold, winter air wafting.
All those times you stood outside and watched your breath
cloud, large animal, moon face, hoof-less. You know his days
go deeper. Snow hole with a man curled in it. Small pack
stitched of deerskin. A fine knife, furs.

Instead of turning right, you stop the car and wait. Something in you:
a shiny, dark-skinned kernel, a need you've put away
like a button from your dead father's coat, a need for history
or flight. No, both. Where you're going, you don't know
but everything you thought was true is false, everything
you've learnt flows out like guts from a split belly,
the strings of intestine you can read your fortune in,
your fate. But you can't look forwards, only back
at the black hulk of the car as you walk off or through
or out. Where are you now? Wait.

The street is unfamiliar; you've never walked here before,
never walked like this with your whole face seeing,
eyes, yes, but also lips, nose, skin, and the skin's soft,
barely visible vellus that marks you out as animal or bird,
a small hawk maybe, all seeing. You can't be sure
but the figure walking over seems to be singing,
mouth wide like a warm dark stone and then the song
coming close, as though the singer's inside you -
you're the lone singer! Be still a while and listen.
Wide streets, wider than you imagined possible,
car-less now, each building flanking something beyond
the mind's eye, something flickering inside an opening.
Never too late. A soul. Small black purse.

When he steps up you know his name is Tog Muhoni
and his life is a fire you forgot to feed, a time you forgot
to live. You drape your sorrow around yourself
but he laughs and with his one good arm
lifts your chin to the sky like a mother might
tilt her child. Somewhere in the other town
your desk is waiting with its papers and books,
a lamp leaning in like an eye piercing the same space
over and over. Tog Muhoni looks at you
as though you've never known looking before.
A blue shawl of looking. An embrace.

Sylvia Linsteadt

Sherds

Now, still, and maybe forever, it is easier to speak of it in poetry.
In pieces.

> *Once you thought you might walk thus for ten thousand leagues*
> *for the beloved, thinking love could be contained*
> *solely in the body of a man*
>
> *Now you see the only desert you could ever survive this way*
> *shedding skin after skin, crushed beneath planetary grinding stones*
> *was kept a country in your own soul, which is but a fragment of Love's,*
> *And that no man nor woman is the final object of this Love*
> *for it arises only and without cease*
> *from the spring of yourself, there beside the oldest stone*
> *there where the snake sheds the skin*
> *beneath the skin*
> *beneath the skin*
> *she thought she was shedding*
>
> *A naked woman is beneath*

'Shattered people are best represented by bits and pieces', Rilke wrote. The same could be said of ancient history. All we have to go on is pottery sherds, and yet the whole vessel is indicated by each of them. I find myself standing somewhere between the two: mine, and the ruins of Minoan Crete, holding the rough bits of a shattered *pithos* in my hands. My known life, or at least the last 11 years of it, all the wine seeping out around my fingers and down the hallways, no way to gather it up again, no way to go back; and a storage vessel used by a clan 4,000 years gone, who spoke a lost language that sounded like water. This metaphor, I think, could be extended to the shattering of ecosystems. When we lose a species, we cannot bring it back. And yet it still lives everywhere, in the negative space. The sharp mountain herbs cut my boots, and in the scratches I feel his absence, where before he would have offered the beeswax oil he used to mend his own. It is in the smallest details that loss will take you to your knees. The pieces left behind.

In the autumn, I ran halfway across the Earth to Crete, to this old, shining, mountainous island. It was the only place that could hold the choice I had made and who I was becoming. I don't know how I knew it, but I knew it. It was the only place where I had seen the primordial face of the female divine so powerfully. It was the only place to hold me still enough so that I could begin to decipher the language scrawled inside that shattered pithos, inside the curved clay, inside my soul, which had been fired at high heat by leaving him, by leaving a life I had made with love for eleven years. Linear A, the script Minoans used to transcribe their language – a pre-Indo-European tongue related probably to the indigenous languages of Europe and Anatolia, before the coming of Aryan cattle-lords from the east – has yet to be deciphered, but sometimes when I look at it, I can feel the way it sang. The language inside me feels the same. Some days I have no notion of its articulation, but I sense the shape of its meaning.

All I know is, the words are sacred on that bit of pottery in my hand, the one that spells what is in me. I may not know them, but they are mine.

Labyrinth

I am poised at the middle of something, balanced at the centre of the *labrys* – those butterfly-wing blades that comprise the double axe, most sacred symbol of primordial Crete and root of the word labyrinth. I don't know anymore if time moves forward and backward, or around and around, as a spiral. Sometimes when I stand among the stones of a Minoan house four millennia empty, or ponder the tsunami caused by the eruption of Thera on Santorini around 1600 BC, which most archaeologists consider the beginning of the end for Minoan civilisation, I feel myself standing just on the other side of a threshold, the two worlds touching fingertips across the aeons, and that it is not a long line between us, but only a series of spirals round and round the sun, so that

I might reach across and touch that other track 4,000 years ago – or 4,000 years beside, in front, within – through a gust in the wind. This gives me a strange sense of hope, of possibility.

Eleven years behind me: the great love of my maiden life. Eleven years ahead: the number of years we have left before life's systems start truly collapsing under the heat and weight of climate chaos.

Chaos, a Greek word, the original chasm from which life arose. First that deep, cosmic darkness. Then a spark; then *eros*; then ground.

Eleven years ago, in the beginning, I loved with original love, first love, love that felt like it came whole out of the beginning of the world, virgin in its intensity, the kind of love that arises directly from an untrammelled heart. Eleven years ago I fell in love and the only words I had to describe it – in long letters sent across the 49 states, from the eastern coast to the western coast where we both grew up – were words for mountains, for dark skies and uncountable stars, for the colour of rain and the scent of redwood forest. I found that my experience of natural beauty and wildness moved in the same language inside me as the language for love.

Oceanic was a word I used often. It was too big, that feeling, to otherwise describe. Metaphor – *you are the pelicans gliding the wave and salt spray at dawn, when the ocean is iridescent, you are that feeling to me* – was how I translated what was in my heart. But maybe they were always, also, one. So that now, leaving, my grief has mountains in it, pelicans, dying oceans, burning skies, and sometimes I cannot tell them apart. Grief makes a doorway. It is personal, and it is planetary. They are like the two paths that meet in the centre of the labyrinth. This heartbreak, the whales washing up one by one on the beaches of our home, somehow make the same word in me. Maybe this is how we learn to love the world. Maybe all I have left is to love the world that way, the metaphor transmuted back to its origin. The face of the beloved, the face of change, the face of the Earth.

Eleven years ago I feared the oceans dying, but did not believe it. I knew we faced the dark mountain, but I could not see it. We slept beside a wild sea, and watched the pelicans, and searched for whales spouting, and it seemed that nothing could touch such waters, nor such love. I wrote stories to face the future, apocalyptic prayers and folktales for what seemed a distant kind of loss. Eleven years, they tell us, but the oceans are already dying, and I understand mostly nothing of what I once thought I knew.

Lamp

At daybreak, among the ruins, a woman sang of lost love with an oil lamp in her hands. She lit the forgotten corridors, the memory of stored wine in *pithoi* as fat and abundant as a Cretan spring, when the poppy flowers ring with their hundred thousand bees.

The woman sang a wound as deep as the gorges of this new country, sudden and sheer.

A stone cast there will echo like an endless cry, and the cry will echo like the longing she had always been afraid to speak – for, if spoken, could it ever be satisfied?

O deep throated chasm, O mother of stone.

The mountains open impossibly and rivers flow where they have settled. Water will find the deepest places that grief has made.

Among the ruined walls, her voice had no bottom. Her lamp burned the oil of her dead foremothers. Yellow crocuses clung to the vertical stones above the chasm, new after rain. They blossomed from nothing, from hard earth, from memory, from everything.

When she sang the chasm grew deeper. She might have fallen in but for the crocus, yellow as fresh honey, as sun. This was an answer to her hunger.

The gorge rang with pollen.

Among the ruined seal-maker's workshops that her oil lamp lit, a cat played cruelly with a dead lizard. The lost lightwell shone among fallen mudbrick walls. Somebody from very long ago heard her singing there, tasted the smoke from her lamp: resin of rock-rose, resin of terebinth. A voice from among the primordial workshops said: *You are just as vast. There is no chasm inside yourself where you cannot go. Make yourself the bell that echoes with ecstasy the deeper it goes. In this, be sated. Spill wine and oil down the centre of the floor. Grief and ecstasy, hunger and satisfaction, they are both the wick and the fuel. You are neither. You are only the lamp. You are only the light. You are only the cupped palm. Live from here, or there can be no renewal.*

Sin

I do not know anymore if I am good. I carry wrongdoing in me, the harm of another heart. I wish I could have done better. I wish I had been braver, clearer, less selfish. I wish I could have caused less pain. I wish I had not caused any pain at all. I have caused so much harm. I must be bad, unworthy, damaged. These thoughts make a dark vortex in my mind most days now. They make a spell. Very often, it takes me all morning to see through them enough to begin again with the work of loving – myself, this world. Most days, most of us, facing 11 years until – the end? Extinction? Unimaginable loss? – probably feel something similar. It's paralysing. I don't know if I am good or I am bad. There is a spell in binaries like this, a spell that makes it hard to see the truth. Dark and light meet at the centre of the labyrinth and form a third thing, more true than either.

So I put my hands on the earth, for there is nothing else to do. Here, right and wrong are both mulch for new life. Soil – xoma (χώμα) in Greek, root of humility, humble, humus – is the goddess of return. What is dead is welcomed here, and remade. Our sins can be laid to rest, if we ask with honesty, *What can I give back to you, right here, little bit of ground? I have been humbled.*

Sometimes, the diagnosis of '11 years left' feels like falling to me, falling with no promise of ground, the loss of everything loved. The stories that once felt mythic now feel lived. But nothing is set in stone. There is a capacity for love in us so great, we would break ourselves apart in the loving. Our hearts can become as big as the Earth. Some nights, when I wake suddenly in the dark, I think I feel the whole curve of the Earth between Crete and the edge of California. Change, loss and renewal break me open that wide. The pottery sherd in my hand, scrawled with unknown writing, is curved that broad. Gaia wrote it.

It does not matter if you are good or you are bad, if you carry guilt or loss or need like a cross, so heavy you can hardly move. Set it down. Save what you can save. Give wildness back to any ground you can. Give shelter to bees, to birds, to spiders. Give solace to stray creatures – the ones inside your soul, and the ones that come to your very literal doorstep. Give honey, give praise, give tears, back to the ground.

Ground

At the bottom of weeping, at the bottom of darkness, where I thought there could be no bottom, is ground.

There I am. In a quiet field watered by the deep spring. The gorge made it. My falling made it, gathering three worlds with me as I fell, until ground was made.

Rest now in the gentle valley where the gorge begins. Among the squash vines, among the orange trees, among the garden rows where three ridges come together, and the plane trees sway, and the old oaks still grow, heavy with birdsong after rain. There is a small stone house, a sky full of stars, the memory of the last sweet summer melons, the green-growing pumpkin, the pink amaranth, a pomegranate tree yellow-leaved with autumn, a warm hearth, a seam of clay in the ground's bed, a lute song to warm the whole night, and my hands full of seeds.

Prayer

Together, we are leaping into what we do not know or understand. May the ground we call forth be loved beyond all reason, beyond all description. May we pray in a language we don't all the way know but sense. We will have our hearts broken into so many pieces they will shine like quartz. May we find enough light there, and enough seeds to share, to shelter and to give sanctuary to life, wherever we go. Maybe being shattered is a way of coming home. How else are we to see the writing inside the pithos, on the broken sherds? How else can we understand what is inside us and what ground we will give our love to?

Sophie McKeand

When We Can No Longer Live in the Reflections of Other People

> Having this kind of dialogue means you don't walk the track you choose. You encounter what is there, going out without a plan, meeting what crosses your path – not just the beautiful, but also the difficult.
>
> – Charlotte Du Cann

It is late April 2018 and I've just finished solo walking (and occasional wild camping) 250km across northern Spain on a pilgrimage to eucalyptus trees. I've now landed in Felixstowe with the aim of finishing this month-long hike by making my way on foot a final 35 miles along the east coast of England to Dunwich. This will include a night camped beneath a dappled silver birch, broken only by bemused horse riders cantering past. Later, I will discover I have walked the final leg of Charlotte and Mark's Sea Kale Project which tells the story of coastal erosion and nuclear power, of local protests and the Transition movement through the life of this stoic plant. Did I know that at the time? It wasn't a conscious decision. Can I tell you that I followed intuition? At the last minute deciding to forego the train and walk instead with no real reason, other than to say that it felt right?

Would I be walking like this if I hadn't encountered Dark Mountain six years previously? If I hadn't read the words of the manifesto that challenged the narrative of progress and our civilisation? When given the truth of a seed we can either cultivate it or bury it deep down and continue life as usual. The problem with burying seeds is that they eventually sprout. When I left Dark Mountain's core group a few years later it was to immerse myself completely in the Welsh community in which I lived. I wanted to explore how bringing creativity into the life of every individual through poetry and theatre, no matter how difficult or wounded they were, could truly change the world, one person at a time. Do I still believe that? Perhaps. Perhaps I failed. Or burned out. Or began to question why I focussed on healing or helping so many others when my own internal landscape felt, in places, increasingly bleak and barren.

As the years have progressed, I've learned to let go of ideas of success and failure, instead working in circles, in fractals, tossing seeds to the wind: I walk out, gather and return; walk out, gather and return. The learning is slow and authentic. Still, I can only explore within the limits of my own imagination, which was completely woven into Wales, into one way of being in the world. What has changed since then is not what I do, but how I do it, and the territory in which I now create.

And so, with no previous experience of walking long distance or solo wild camping and no map except some random conversations with strangers, I follow the blue circles with yellow arrows of the Suffolk Coast Path that echo the blue background with yellow-shelled waymarkers of the Camino de Santiago I've just left behind. I do not yet know the names of the birds who warble from the long grasses or wade in the muddy riverbanks, I don't even know the wild grasses, but I am determined to learn, to shift focus from a world dominated by the minds and words and needs of people, to a life immersed in the sounds and shapes of the natural landscape and all who inhabit her. Over this month I have walked myself into the dreaming of the land until, on the last day hiking with a 17kg backpack, my feet are so sore I have to adopt a kind of lizard-on-hot-sand hop-and-skip-along. Finally, I see Charlotte and Mark waving down to me through a thin, grey, rain-soaked day, from the Dunwich cliffs.

Over a year later, I'm writing this sitting with my partner and two rescue hounds in our home-on-wheels on a quiet riverbank north of Marseille, France. Everything we own is in this van. We have minimised our life to an extreme extent and have been slow-travelling nomads exploring Europe since November 2017 with no plans to stop. Andy is photographing the host of European bee-eaters flashing bronze and blue across an aquamarine river; a white tailed eagle swings lazy circles in a blue sky as cotton-like poplar seeds snow onto a family of white egrets fishing in the river's shallows; endless swallows tailspin as a bolt of brilliant yellow signals a golden oriole cutting a straight line across this scene. Later I swim naked in the river and realise I know all of these names because they mean something to me, because, in order to better know myself, I thought I had to look for my reflection in the words and deeds of other people; what Dark Mountain taught me is that the land is my teacher, my mentor, my guide. I have let go of the need to control, change, or understand the behaviour of other people; instead I immerse in the beauty of this singular moment. Perhaps this is all there is in the world. I hope this might be enough.

Catrina Davies

Lost in Transit

The wrong side of too far

> I never saw a discontented tree. They grip the ground as though they liked it, and though fast rooted they travel about as far as we do.
>
> – John Muir

On the way to the Dhamma hall, I can see the peaks of distant mountains rising out of forested slopes. There are stragglers on the ridges of the mountains, lonely pines walking forever upwards into the hazy blue sky. In the distance, about three km away, the red roofs and white walls of Candeleda shimmer in the heat, a little cluster of humanity among the mountains and trees and dusty red earth. For once, I know exactly where I am. I am 400 miles, three mountain ranges, two thunderstorms, five loaves of bread, three kilos of cheese, nine bottles of cold *cerveza*, one new tyre, one golden eagle and ten long days by bicycle from the city of Bilbao. Bilbao is a 24-hour journey by sea from Plymouth, which is a two-hour journey by train from Penzance, which is an hour by bicycle – or three hours on foot – from the shed where I live.

I'm here to practice sitting still and doing nothing. In a fast-moving world, full of very busy people, sitting still and doing nothing requires a lot of practice. The purpose is to develop awareness, and awareness hurts. Perception is suffering. The point of meditation is to develop the ability to accept life as it is, not as we would like it to be. Megaphones can wake us up, but to stay awake we need to learn how to hear the truth buried in our animal cells.

Sacca means truth, and the truth of Dhamma Sacca is long yellow foxgloves, wild lavender, giant ants, cornflowers, rugged mountains bathed in constant sunlight, cuckoos, nightjars, flies, and sheep with heavy bells around their necks.

Last night, I slept outside with the scorpions on the cold, dusty ground, because the other women in the dormitory were snoring like elephants. I dreamt I left by mistake. I cycled into the mountains on my own and cycled up into the hazy sky, like the outlying trees. The dream turned into a nightmare; I couldn't find my way back. Now it is five in the morning and I'm standing behind a trestle table with the rising sun in my eyes, wearing an apron and shelling garlic with Suzi and Marina.

The bell rings for the first group sitting of the day. We leave our aprons on the hooks by the kitchen door and make our way through the morning to the Dhamma hall. I settle onto my cushion, along with several hundred strangers from at least a dozen different countries. We sit together in silence for an hour, watching thoughts flicker across the surface of our minds, like reflections on a lake. It takes everything I've got not to open my eyes and look at the clock, not to fidget, stretch out my legs, manufacture an excuse to get up and run away.

*

> Rockets are cool. There's no getting around that.
>
> – Elon Musk

At the Guggenheim in Bilbao, I shot upwards in a glass elevator towards Rothko's famous rectangles. According to the audio guide, the rectangles were Rothko's way of giving up on trying to be rational. He wanted to go straight to the powerful emotional heart of things, which he was convinced was more real than reality. I paused on one of the gallery's many balconies to watch a group of middle-aged women carrying identical handbags with gold clasps get lost in 'The Matter of Time'. 'The Matter of Time creates a dizzying, unforgettable sensation of space in motion', said the disembodied voice.

Leaving Bilbao took half a day. The city was soaking into the surrounding landscape, like red wine on a white shirt, and my map had not kept up. I got lost crossing and recrossing a six-lane motorway. I had to carry my bike – with its overflowing panniers that weighed nearly as much as me – up a long flight of steps. The bike tipped over backwards, because of gravity.

I found a road that followed a river, bought a coffee, and drank it standing up with the sun on my face. The air smelled of eucalyptus. There were blackbirds singing, and half a dozen cuckoos, each sounding a slightly different note and with slightly different timing. Cuck cuck oo cuck oo oo cuck cuck oo cuck cuck cuck oo. There was a dark-haired woman, standing in a bed of rock roses, wearing bright red lipstick and a flowered cotton dress. She stared at me with an anguished expression, like a character out of a Pedro Almodóvar film.

The woman reminded me of a Turkish friend who once stopped a mounted policeman and asked him how she could get a license to ride a horse across London. What kind of test would she have to pass? The policeman said there was no test and no license. The rules for riding a horse across London are the same as the rules for riding a bike.

We bonded over this, my friend and I, trading images of office workers on horseback, cantering through the streets of London, hustling car drivers, bunching up behind traffic lights, the horses snorting and pawing the ground. Horses would be cheaper than public transport, better for air pollution than cars, more fun than bikes. They could graze in the parks, so there'd be no need for lawnmowers and glyphosate. We could grow vegetables with their dung. We could use them to go on holiday, carrying our tents in panniers, or they could pull trailers. Eventually we remembered that the whole point of the last 200 years had been to move on from horses and carts.

Progress is often measured in terms of mobility. Twenty-first century civilisation is built on the collapse of distance. Money makes nothing of time and space; faster, cheaper transport is an indicator of economic growth. The EU spends £30 billion every year subsidising aviation, with more and more people choosing to go on long-haul mini-breaks, according to Thomas Cook. A weekend in Thailand or Mexico, with most of it spent crumpled up in a metal box.

The first rule of travel is knowing where you're going. The second is knowing when you get there. The third is knowing when you've gone too far. From the wrong side of too far, the collapse of distance looks like the collapse of civilisation. Oil wars, refugee camps, hurricanes, wildfires, famine, depression, suicide. Progress measured in terms of loss. Forty million songbirds. Gone. One-and-a-half acres of forest per second. Gone. One species every 20 minutes. Gone. We're going so fast now, making such good time. Soon we'll wipe ourselves out. Or crash through into a whole other dimension, like Concorde used to crash through the sound barrier when I was growing up, every night at 9 pm. Boom.

According to Elon Musk, chief executive of Tesla and SpaceX, the fastest way to warm Mars sufficiently for humans to survive on its barren, freezing craters is to drop thermonuclear weapons on its poles.

*

> You are free, and that is why you are lost.
> – Kafka

I'd been following signs to Amurrio for so long that when I reached Amurrio I kept on following signs for Amurrio until I was lost in it, wondering where the road had gone. I consulted the map, and then I consulted an old man who was standing on the doorstep of his house, watching me. I showed him my map, and he said the word Amurrio over and over again, until I finally understood that I was there. The next town on my route south was Orduña. The old man pointed out the road I should take. There were no contours on the map, and the old man gave no indication of what lay ahead.

Spain is a mountainous country. I would cycle over a dozen huge passes before I returned to England, most of them more than 2000 m above sea level. I would get used to spending whole mornings pedalling slowly uphill. I would stop swearing and crying, and learn to pace myself. The skin on my bum would turn hard and calloused. I would use muscles I didn't know I possessed. But first I had to adjust to this new way of travelling, and adjusting is never easy.

The Puerto d'Orduña was 900m above sea level, a wall of rock rising dramatically out of the flat plains, like a giant door in the sky. An hour passed. Then another one. Cars flashed their lights and honked their horns. I couldn't tell if they were cheering or jeering and I didn't care. I was hungry, thirsty, hot and exhausted. I tried pushing, but pushing was even harder than pedalling. Afternoon turned into evening. I had no idea where I was going to sleep that night; all that mattered was getting somewhere, getting to the top, getting high.

On a train or in a car, the difference between Madrid and Candeleda is less than an hour, with Madrid being the nearest airport. On a bicycle, the difference between Madrid and Candeleda is about two days, or one-and-a-half if the wind is behind you and you don't get lost. The wind was against me, and strong, and I did get lost. I got lost on dirt tracks that all looked the same. It was late afternoon again when the dirt tracks came to an abrupt end.

I found an old woman, chewing on a piece of straw. She cackled when I pointed to the small mountain that stood between me and the campsite where I was hoping to spend the night. There was no way over the mountain, she said, only a path too steep and narrow for my bicycle. I would have to find my way back through the labyrinth of dirt tracks, then skirt around the base of the mountain on the main road. Devastated, I measured the extra distance with my thumb, pressing it against my torn map – 40km, give or take. I'd already cycled 100km that day. It was my own fault – I'd wanted a shortcut so badly I'd invented a route that wasn't there.

It started raining soon after I found my way out of the tangled dirt tracks and onto the main road. Cars passed me too fast and too close. When I pulled into a layby to check my progress against the map, a man in a ramshackle jeep pulled up next to me. 'Are you lost?' he asked, in Spanish. I showed him where I was trying to get to; the village where I thought (hoped) there was a campsite. He pointed over the road at a track that led off into another cluster of hills. 'It's much closer if you go that way.' He looked at my tyres, weighing up whether they'd make it. 'You want a lift?'

I knew I shouldn't get into a jeep at dusk with a strange man who didn't speak my language, and let him drive me up a dirt track into some lonely hills, but I was very tired. As it happened, the bike and I didn't fit in the jeep, so he tied my bike to the back bumper and dragged me. At first, I was elated to be going so fast uphill without even having to pedal. Then I was terrified to be going so fast uphill with no way of stopping. The track was heavily potholed. My bike was old and had no suspension. The rack that was carrying my panniers came loose and jammed into the back wheel. I almost fell, but managed to save myself. At the top of the hill, we finally stopped. My legs were shaking. He pointed out the village, which was just visible in the distance. He untied my bike and fixed the rack back on with cable ties. *Gracias. Ciao.*

Much later, after I'd put up my tiny tent in the sideways rain, and bought beer and salt and vinegar crisps in the deserted campsite bar, I allowed myself to feel the fear I'd been suppressing. The fear of yesterday and today and tomorrow. The fear of things breaking and falling apart. The fear of being abducted. I was still shaking. But there was satisfaction, too. I spread the wet map out on the bar and used my thumb to measure how far I'd travelled already, compared to how far I still had to travel. The whole of Spain was about as wide as my hand. I could have flown from Bristol to Madrid for less than £50. It would have taken a couple of hours. Sweden has a whole new word for the thing that stopped me. *Flygskam.* Flight shame. The difference between ignorance and denial.

I slept hard that night and woke up early. The rain had stopped. I crawled out of my tent and lay on the grass in my sleeping bag with my eyes closed, listening to a blackbird. The day was long and lonely. Miles of empty dirt tracks, forests of pine and eucalyptus, then a long river valley, the road swooping to sea level, then climbing suddenly, swooping, climbing, swooping, climbing. The constant sound of blackbirds singing. Pain in my knees. I stopped to rest and drink water. I chanced to look upwards and was gifted my first ever sighting of a golden eagle. Above it, the contrails from two aeroplanes made a cross in the sky.

The Latin word *avis* means bird. Aviation means bird-in-action. Legend has it that Leonardo da Vinci once dreamed he could fly. 'Once you have tasted flight,' he is supposed to have said afterwards, 'you will forever walk the earth with your eyes turned skyward, for there you have been, and there you will always long to return.'

*

> So we drove on towards death through the cooling twilight.
> – F. Scott Fitzgerald

Two weeks later, I pump up my tyres and say goodbye to Suzi and Marina. I stop in Candeleda to buy fruit and bread and cheese; more food than I can squeeze into my overflowing panniers. After ten days of withdrawal, the world seems huge and new and terribly beautiful. Also, I'm very hungry.

I hurl myself at the Puerto de Serranillos, which forms part of the Spanish version of the Tour de France. Thunder rumbles around terraces of olives and vines. The road climbs steeply into the clouds. Signs with pictures of bicycles on them count down the kilometres: 23, 22, 21. I stop on a stone bridge four km from the summit and eat an orange. It's raining. I go too fast down the other side of the mountain. I take my hands off the handlebars. I sit on a red plastic chair and drink an orange juice and soda water and listen to rain pelting the plastic awning. I ask the bartender about campsites. There aren't any.

I sleep on a rocky outcrop crawling with ants. In the morning, I sit outside a café in a small town called Bergondo, dipping a croissant in my coffee. I watch people hurrying to work, taking their children to school, getting on and off buses, going in and out of shops. I feel distanced from them after my night under the stars. I feel immune. From my new vantage point, reached after ten days of sitting still and doing nothing, I can see that campsites are nothing but expensive cages, ringed with high fences, an illusion of safety full of overflowing bins and cars and cigarette butts.

The vehicles on the road up to Lagos de Covadonga are mostly enormous white camper vans or boy racers with souped-up engines and shiny hubcaps. It's seven in the evening and a crazy time to start cycling up a 12 km vertical hill, but Covandonga is full of tourists. Wild camping is technically illegal in Spain and I don't want to get fined.

The campervans and boy racers pass me again, this time going down. Stars come out, one by one, littering the dark blue sky. I stop to take photographs of the road I've cycled up. I can see all the way to the sea. The laybys have signs in them, *No Camping*. I keep pedalling, up into the darkness. Up and up and up. A tatty red Berlingo van passes me for the second time. Going down this time, with the lights on. It makes me ache for home.

My own tatty Berlingo van is blue. I mainly use it for storing the things that don't fit in my shed: bike, gardening tools, shoes, coats, hats, surfboards. My van is 19 years old. It has travelled 180,000 miles, 50,000 of them with me. I could have done two laps of the Earth for that, one around the equator and one going pole to pole. Instead, I've mostly driven in small circles within a 20-mile radius of my shed.

In the month it takes me to cycle to Candeleda and back, including ten days of silence, my fellow Brits have driven 27 *billion* miles (on an island that's just 800 miles long). Nearly four million have travelled at least two hours every day for work. Worldwide, highway vehicles have released about 140 million tonnes of greenhouse gases into the atmosphere.

When I was little, we had a Datsun Sunny. It was so rusty Mum got pulled over by the police every time she left the house. Later we had a Citroën 2CV that went round corners on two wheels, then a bright red Talbot Samba, then a white Ford Fiesta. They're all in landfill now. The Berlingo will probably be in landfill soon. It doesn't lock anymore, and it sometimes makes a grinding noise like a tractor, for no fathomable reason. Maybe by the time it dies, I'll be able to afford to replace it with an electric one.

Lithium for electric car batteries is mined in South America, then shipped to Canada for refining, then to China, where the batteries are made, then to North America, where most of the cars are made. Fifty-eight per cent of the world's cobalt is mined in the Democratic Republic of Congo (DRC). The soil, air and water in the mining area of the DRC is so toxic, it is ranked as one of the ten most polluted places in the world. The mining industry has helped fuel a conflict that has ruined millions of lives. And it's only just begun. On current trends, the demand for cobalt will massively exceed existing reserves by 2050. Given the realities of battery production and disposal, and the fact that around 50% of UK electricity is still generated by fossil fuels, electric cars are only about 20% less ruinous than ordinary cars.

*

> The error is taking the body to be the cause of bondage, when the real source of trouble lies in the mind.
>
> – Bhikkhu Bodhi

It's my last night before catching the ferry home and I'm camped on a low grassy headland at the back of a wild and empty beach. I freewheeled down a long, bumpy track to get here, then carried my bike through a patch of gorse and brambles. I wanted to get myself out of sight of a line of camper vans parked where the tarmac runs out. Apparently, I won't get fined if I'm far enough away from a road, because Spanish policemen never get out of their cars.

The sea is flat. The air is perfectly still. There are clouds on the horizon, but I'm too busy eating cherries and feeling smug about myself and worrying about the pain in my knees to notice how they're stacking up and causing the sea to darken and a westerly breeze to start. My tent is on its last legs. I redo the gaffer tape on a snapped pole and find rocks to use in place of missing pegs. I'm glad this is the last time I'll have to put it up.

The sea is not flat anymore. There are small waves breaking against the rocks that line the shore. When I get home I'll be able to go surfing. My skin crackles with anticipation.

Surfing is a kind of travelling, the kind where you get transported, but end up exactly where you started. With my eyes closed and my legs crossed, I imagine myself stuck to the surface of the spinning earth, surfing it through time. Then I imagine time travelling through me, marking my face, wearing out my joints and my heart, depositing memories in hard-to-reach parts of my brain, like the sand that gets stuck between my toes. If time is a wave, travelling through space, then sooner or later it will break. The beginning, middle and end of life on Earth will be tumbled together. Everything will become nothing. It happens every day out in the cosmos: red giants, white dwarves, black holes. I wonder what becomes of the timeless things when time stops. The poems, jokes and memories, the myths and legends and universal plots, the perfect little songs we sang, in perfect harmony.

I climb into my tiny tent and close the broken zips as best I can, using hair slides. Insects get in anyway and bite me, but I fall asleep in spite of them, exhausted from my long journey.

I'm woken three hours later by the sound of angry waves hurling themselves at the headland and a furious wind ripping into my dreams. The rain, when it comes, is loud and frantic, followed by rumbling thunder and flashes of lightning. I make myself as flat as possible, spreading my arms and legs wide, in an effort to stop the sides of the tent lifting up and taking off.

I have to wee. I try to focus my attention on the sound of the sea, on the rhythmic crashing and scraping of the waves. It's no good. I wriggle out of my sleeping bag and remove the hair slides holding the broken zips together. I get to my feet and lean back with my arms out, letting the air hold me up. Pieces of foam swirl and dance in the moonlight, like snowflakes. Behind me the tent flaps and bends and strains against the rocks and pegs that are holding it down.

It's hard staying grounded, alone in a storm on the edge of the Bay of Biscay. Hard being the still point of a world in furious flight. Hard listening to the savage reality of time and space and distance coming together and breaking. Hard to stand on the threshold of a terrifying future and stare unflinchingly into the abyss.

But *existence* is hard. We all have to live under the shadow of death. How we conduct ourselves here and now, during this moment of profound global crisis, is crucial. This is the sixth mass extinction, not the first. It has happened before and it can happen again – will happen again if we're too slow to wake up. We can fly in panicked circles, like a bird trapped in a greenhouse, kicking against the laws and limitations of nature. Or we can grow up, learn humility, sit still, do nothing, make time for the future to heal.

Cate Chapman

Understanding Survival

Understand: she survives
in the blankness, this girl, in unbecoming – she lies
back flat against smooth grey planks, on this occasion,
and gazing into a perfectly blue sky until it's over,
crow-mind wheeling up in the silence,
high and untouchable.
Understand: the weight of her body
is lost to her, along with all the rest of it – and this
is where the wound is:
the sinew binding body-mind to spirit quietly
mangled, like a little death.
Why shouldn't we suffer, in this toddler world
of grab and snatch? In this culture
that takes whatever it wants, and us included.

Understand: a film of shame covers everything,
fine and grey as dust, and as cloying, as slow to settle –
not just coating skin, but eyeballs,
stomach, roof of the mouth,
imperceptibly clouding every experience.
Understand that this is a spiritual injury,
just as all atrocities are on some level spiritual injuries.

Later, she duck-dives in the cold brown sea
by the Palace Pier, and rises
otter-slick and momentarily renewed,
heathen and baptismal and fire-bright,
swimming her way back into reality,
body like a grip let go, like an open palm,

empty of nuance or history or consequence,
burning with life and sensation and
spread out, vast, between the cold sea
and a sky that reaches out
forever, into the unimaginable universe –
spreading out infinitely
like prayer

Dougie Strang

Cleaning the Cailleach's Well

The wind was fierce on the ridge, so that I was glad of the ballast of my rucksack. At the summit I sheltered in the lee of the cairn, crouching among stones and moss, the tiny green hands of alpine lady's mantle. I stayed too late on top, thrilled by the views as the sun set behind the peaks and ridges of Lochaber. Below me, the moor seemed to heave and shift in the dark, as though it was unmoored, as though the lochs dotted across it were the only fixed points, glinting the last of the light.

I dropped down from the summit onto the western slope of the ridge, searching amongst banks of turf and exposed swathes of peat. Water seeped to the surface in dips and creases but you wouldn't call them pools. It was late and time to stop, even before I stumbled into the bog. When I pulled out my leg it was cast in wet, black peat, heavy, like a false leg, or someone else's, so that I had to shake it until it felt like my own. I pitched my tent in the dark on a patch of firm ground, pulled off wet clothes and crept into my sleeping bag. My head torch threw shadows that billowed with the tent in the wind.

By early morning the wind had eased and cloud huddled around the ridge. I was inside the cloud, the air wet and cold. There was no summit or sight of other mountains. I cut out a small circle of turf on a level bank and unpacked the bag of kindling and the half-dozen split birch logs that I'd carried in my rucksack. My fire was a compact sun, unnaturally bright against the grey of the mist. I boiled water in a pot, willing the flames to lift the cloud and conjure the actual sun. I drank tea, ate oatcakes and a cold, sweet apple. With the last of the logs burning, I walked around the fire three times and then jumped over it: just a man leaping a fire on a mountain in the clouds, on the morning of the first of May.

A decade ago I began to educate myself about climate change, habitat destruction, ecocide. It hurt my head to think about it but how could you not? I read the books and articles and learned that the world was unravelling. I didn't sleep well. Then I read a manifesto by two writers I hadn't heard of. They were digging down, unearthing the truth that something had been broken that wouldn't be fixed simply by reducing carbon emissions. I got involved with the project the writers started, making performances for its festivals. This has led to other collaborations with writers and artists, both within Dark Mountain and without. I've tried to make work that responds to the unravelling, that reminds us of our place within, not separate from, the natural world; that humbles us. In doing so, I've found that performance can happen anywhere: in a theatre, a festival, on wasteland at the edge of a city on a Saturday night; and that sometimes performance becomes ceremony, and has to do with old-fashioned ideas of gratitude, obligation, propitiation.

I took down my tent and packed my rucksack, waited until the fire's embers died and then replaced the circle of turf, tramping it down. The wind shifted, thinning the cloud so that I could look around and gauge my position relative to the map I was holding. I was in the right place, marked Fuaran nan Cailleach, 'the well of the Cailleach'. In Gaelic, *fuaran* usually means a well in its natural state, an undug pool or spring, so it was possible that the peat bog I'd stumbled into the night before, with its few inches of surface water, was all there was to find. As for the Cailleach, she's a versatile figure in Scottish folklore: wise-woman, crone of winter; but also land-shaping giant and, especially here in Lochaber, mistress of the deer.

The side of the mountain steepened below me. I clambered down to where a stream flowed into a gully between two crags, and then followed its course back up amongst the folds of the slope, hoping it might lead to what I was looking for. I startled a mountain hare that was crouched in a dip to the left of the stream, encroaching on the tolerated space between us as though I'd nudged a tripwire. It sprang away into the mist and left my body charged with adrenalin.

The Cailleach's well is tucked in a hollow so that it's hidden from above and below. At a short distance you would walk by without noticing it. It's a small, oval pool, gravel-lined and clear, like a portal. The stream I'd followed poured from the lip of it. The water tasted like stone. I filled my water bottle and cupped my hands and washed my face. Mindful of local tradition, that refers to the need for the well to be cleaned at Beltane, I rolled up my sleeves and began to clear silt from the bottom of the pool. After a few minutes of scooping and splashing my arms were numb with cold. When I stopped, the pool returned to stillness.

It all needs doing: performance, ceremony, acts of creativity and beauty, whether for an audience or alone on the side of a mountain; all of it a vessel for our grief and for our joy.

Dropping beneath the cloud, I followed the stream back down to the gully. Gleann Iolairean, 'the eagles' glen', opened below me. A bird flew past, contouring the crags: a swallow, unexpected in this place and at this height. It tilted its body away from me in alarm, flashing its orange breast and looking back with a tiny, black eye. Small, quick life, heart the size of a tic tac, following an old ellipse from Scotland to Africa and back, carrying the sun from the south on its breast. Now I was blessed. Now it was the first day of summer.

KAHN & SELESNICK

Quantum Augury

In the high mountains, the augur spins two balls, one representing the particle, the other, the wave. As in quantum physics, time may be experienced either in a linear, flowing fashion (the wave) or in its entirety in a single instantaneous flash (the particle). During the later, the observer ceases to exist in any meaningful way, making it impossible to retain the auguries obtained in this state. This does not stop augurs from being attracted to this method, as it is thought to be accurate down to the tiniest microscopic details.

(see story overleaf)

Kahn & Selesnick

To Become an Augur

If you desire to become an augur, follow these instructions: first, take a comforting thought or feeling and examine it in your mind until you realise it is a lie. Do this until no pleasurable thoughts remain. In your newfound state of misery, take an unhappy observation and examine it in your mind until you realise it too is a lie. Continue until all miserable thoughts and feelings are vanquished. At this stage you will find yourself alone on an infinite plain devoid of vegetation, with no city or ocean dancing on the horizon. If you wait until time ceases to exist, a speck will appear in the far distance; eventually, as it draws nearer, you will see that it is in fact a horse; nearer still, that it appears to be dragging something behind it by a fraying rope. As it draws alongside you, you see that this thing appears to resemble a stump of twisted flesh, like an ostrich turned inside out, or the parts of a rotted crocodile, sewn back together by someone with no knowledge of the appearance of the original animal. With a start you realise that this thing is still alive; it is emitting a low hum. Actually less a hum than a song, but not in a traditional sense. In fact, it more resembles a faceted sound in which each facet in turn reveals a hundred more facets; or a bloom – not like a flower, but like jellyfish, or algae. As you stand listening, you become aware that this sound (is it a sound?) seems to be emanating from your own chest. You reach down and carefully untie the rope from the crocodile-stump thing, bind it around your torso, lie down and wait for the horse to continue its endless march across the broken landscape…

KAHN & SELESNICK

The Augury of Collapse

If you are to see that which is to come, you must stop the world; you must take your feet off the pedals of the Earth and stop it spinning. If you are in the grocer's, stop pushing your cart and stare off into space, oblivious to the other shoppers. If you are walking down the crowded avenue, stop, lay down in the middle of the sidewalk, and watch the clouds slowly pass over the tops of the old tenements. Abandon your tools and walk down to the water's edge. As the momentum of the world slows for just one infinitesimal moment, others will join you until everyone is staring off into the distance, waiting for that incomprehensible event we have all felt lurking beneath the surfaces of our lives to finally reveal itself.

KAHN & SELESNICK

The Martyr's Augury

According to the most ancient of traditions, rather than being a ruler, the king was a sacrificial victim offered up (and frequently eaten) to maintain the prosperity of his people. It was the very power and dignity bestowed upon him that gave his sacrifice its unique power. For this ritual to attain its fullest force, the sacrifice must be performed by the queen, who hunts the king in the primordial bogs and consumes him once he is martyred. The issue of this union is the red queen, who is in fact neither king nor queen but androgyne. By this process the flesh (beast) is transubstantiated into spirit (god).

KATIE IONE CRANEY

Wetland for Christine Byl, for her essay,
'Crane, Water, Change: A Migratory Essay'

Photographs, blueberry-dyed gauze, found maps of Denali, silver leaf, and encaustic on hand-cut scrap metal

Observing nuanced environmental change in Denali National Park, author Christine Byl links crane and cranberry as 'the eater and the eaten, a berry connects the Athabaskan and the European, a bird connects a berry to a mother tongue.' This piece is part of *Landfalls*, a series of dedications to Alaskan women authors and storytellers.

KIT BOYD
Reading Dark Mountain
Hand-painted print

In the scene a figure reads Dark Mountain under a tree beside a secluded house. This is a real landscape I visit often. In the distance, the dark mountain is Cader Idris. It is a refuge from reality, travelling back into a tranquil pre-industrial world and the perfect place to read these reflective stories.

KATE WALTERS

Woman of the Horses

Watercolour on gessoed-paper

I made this work after time spent on Orkney and visiting the ancient site the Ness of Brodgar. I learned about the connections between the earlier peoples and their animals, and in particular a structure of animal bones they left behind when they left the site for good (we don't know why).

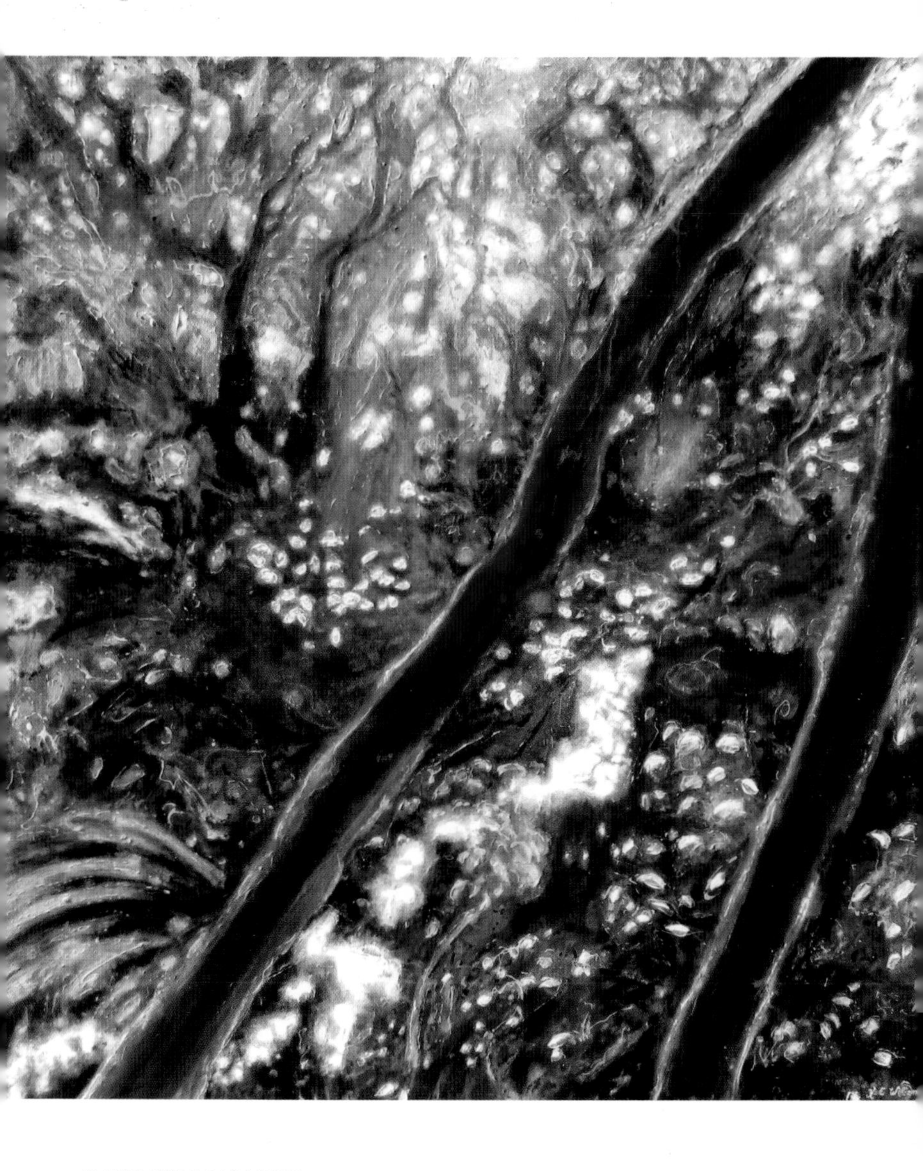

KATE WLLIAMSON

Forest Lights

Acrylic on canvas

In contrast to humanity's rigid obsession with order, this painting is a celebration of biodiversity, set in Waipori Falls, New Zealand where I live. All the intricate abundance and variety of life all living together amongst a scintillating kaleidoscope of reflecting surfaces, of broad, shiny leaves, smooth glimmering rocks and sparkling water.

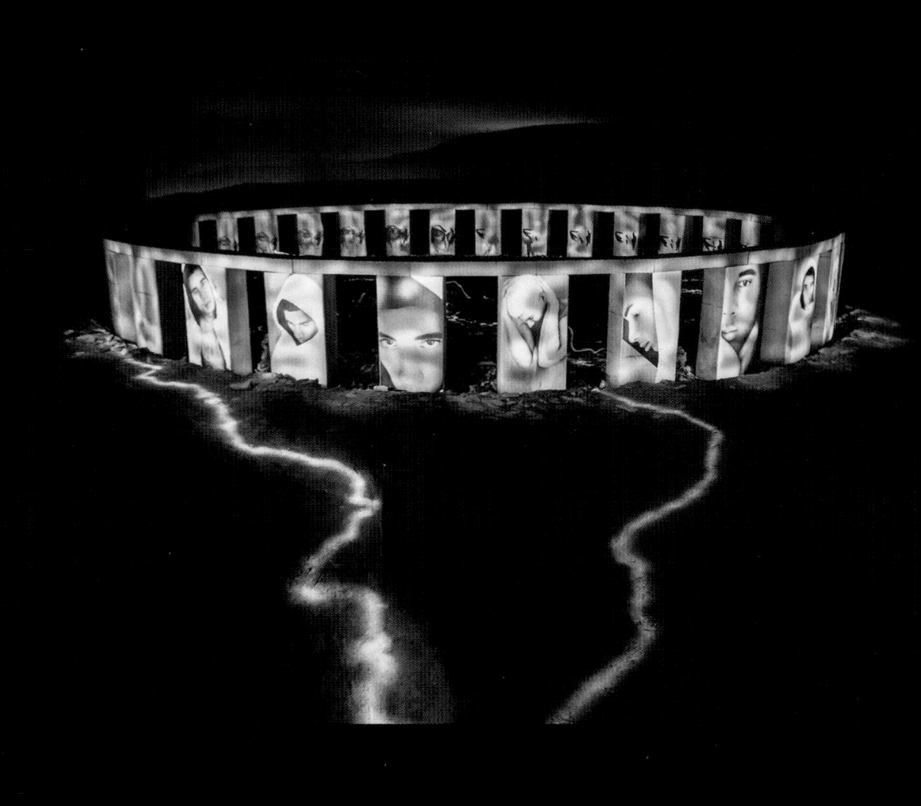

GAVIN LEANE
Achill Henge
Long-exposure photograph, using light painting

Leane captured the Henge while it was temporarily adorned with images of emigration, decay and lost youth from Joe Caslin's public art project, *Our Nation's Sons.*

Tom Smith

Palimpsest

I was certain I was going to crash into the sea. I had already been driving into nothingness when a storm arrived with the kind of wind that the west of Ireland knows best: blowing in all directions simultaneously, buffeting the car with playful ferocity. In the infinite darkness, with raindrops darting everywhere at once, all sense of direction evaporated. My headlights gave me nothing. Left, right, up, down? Who could tell? So I kept the steering wheel level for as long as possible, waiting for some break in the vortex, hoping not to meet a watery end.

When daylight arrived, I looked at a map and was embarrassed to discover that, though bound for one of Ireland's most westerly islands – Achill, County Mayo – I hadn't yet been anywhere near the sea when the winds began. This landless, featureless nothingness was an effect produced by the road being raised high, safely out of reach of the all-consuming bog which coats these parts. There had not been a single visible light or landmark, not because I had been teetering on a cliff at the edge of the Old World, but merely because vast expanses of this corner of the country are characterised by what, to the civilised eye, is sodden nothingness. No trees, no shrubs, no buildings, no lights, no other roads. And no people, for that matter. Just bog, a quagmire of decay. The city of Dublin and its surrounds have a population density of about 3,677 people per square kilometre; County Mayo has just 22.

The end of the future

It's November. Every muscle of my body is tense, braced against the damp cold. The everywhere-wind hasn't left, but in the morning light I crawl out of bed in an icy hostel and head out anyway. The spaciousness of Achill's yellow-grey landscape is enchanting. It's closer to Alaska or Mars than the green rolling fields of the Ireland I am from. However,

I'm not here to be enchanted. I am instead hunting out an imprint of humanity: a concrete ruin which I've been hearing stories about, and which I promised myself I would one day see in person.

Turning right after the church in the village of Pollagh, on the south-west corner of the island, I take the car as far along a bouncy bog road as I can. A few hundred metres up the hill, and with the underside of the car scraping rock, I'm forced to continue on foot, guided by the anonymous kindness of hand-painted signs. I've been waiting more than a year, and now Achill Henge stands before me in all of its brute monumentality. A blot on the landscape. A hole torn into the hillside. I don't care. I love it.

The builder of this 100-metre diameter concrete replica of Stonehenge was a bankrupt property developer, Joe McNamara, who grew up on the island. Facing financial ruin in the wake of the 2008 crisis, he called in some last-minute favours to have it constructed in November 2011. Built over just two days, the Henge's 30 enormous concrete pillars were raised as a symbolic tomb for the Celtic Tiger, Ireland's construction-led economic 'miracle' of the 1990s and 2000s. The richest country in the world, economists raved at the time, although the reality was always somewhat less lustrous. It was a case of *Father Ted* meets *The Wolf of Wall Street*: dodgy dealings seemingly harder to turn down than Mrs. Doyle's cups of tea. *Oh, go on!* Meanwhile, it took a comedian called Tommy Tiernan to adequately capture just one example of the absurd new dynamics of daily life: Irish people, carried away by what are colloquially called 'notions', suddenly began appearing on the ski slopes of Europe, dressed in the finest discount Aldi equipment. You just knew something was wrong.

The landscape of every county became a flurry of activity, building sites on every corner, apprentices hired by the dozen. When the global financial crisis turned miracle to mirage, the cranes became still. Thousands lost their jobs and Ireland defaulted back to being a place which people left to find livelihoods elsewhere. In the aftermath, the nation appeared not just angry at having to foot the bill of speculative greed, but spiritually lost, unsure of its place in the world. Ireland was bestially downgraded from a Tiger to one of the PIIGS (Portugal, Ireland, Italy, Greece and Spain). A whole way of life had crumbled, illusions evaporating seemingly overnight, to be replaced by a decade of bewilderment and cultural trauma. The capital-wielding class was protected, of course, but the rest of the island was left to pray to the economic gods that growth and prosperity would return.

The Henge was a protest; a record, in concrete, of this collapse. A symbol of a 'prosperous' national future which never arrived, it is a contemporary ruin and perhaps the world's most prominent commemorative monument to economic collapse and the fallacies of a growth-based economy. If you stand in the centre of it and clap, you hear sharp echoes of a time that saw so many grey, concrete, unfinished property developments abandoned. For years, these uninhabitable 'ghost estates' would haunt the landscape of every county on the island of Ireland. The future foreclosed before the moneyed existence these houses were supposed to be a part of could ever arrive. The Henge, too, is unfinished. After the outer circle was completed, the local authority intervened. McNamara had previously run into legal trouble after driving a cement truck into the gates of the Irish parliament, raging against the role of the banks in the crisis. He ended up in prison for refusing to take down his latest creation, subsequently fleeing to England. He argued that it was a contemplative ornamental garden, and thus exempt from planning permission.

The 'Jared Diamond' ruin

If you head across the swing bridge that links Achill to the mainland and travel north, you come to a halt at some of Europe's grandest sea cliffs. Dún briste, the broken fort – a 50-metre-high sea stack – emerges out of the sea, telegraphing 350 million years of indifference. The sight is an unexpected bonus. I cross the empty road and head towards a modernist interpretive centre jutting out of the bog, shaped like a pyramid, the only visible sign of Céide Fields.

In the 1930s, a local schoolmaster, Patrick Caulfield, had been cutting turf in this area. As he sliced deeper into the earth's skin, he noticed conspicuous lines of stone. His discovery was first excavated by his son, Seamus, with the scale of the agricultural community that was discovered being startlingly vast. These early inhabitants were using around 1,000 hectares of land to graze dairy cows and grow ancestral wheat grains. But I expected something grander from what is often described as the 'most extensive Neolithic monument in the world'. The site is comprised of a series of newly constructed wooden walkways over the blanket bog, with poles indicating where the submerged boundaries of fields lie. An occasional open excavation reveals the footings of Neolithic dwellings; unlike the Celtic Tiger's ghost estates, this site had been well-inhabited for centuries.

While visual displays and information panels attempt to stir interest in the daily lives of these distant ancestors, my gaze is instead drawn to a brief paragraph on the decline and subsequent abandonment of this once-thriving community. I think about Jared Diamond's book *Collapse*, which famously presented numerous striking parables of societal collapse induced by environmental short-sightedness; the figure of an Easter Islander caught up in a culture of spiralling competition is perhaps the most famous. Cutting down the island's last tree, he or she acts without thought for how the community will survive in the future. What better parallel for the ecocide perpetuated by industrial civilisation? While Diamond's book was acclaimed, the simplicity of its examples have since been questioned by other scholars. For the sake of a moral tale on Easter Island, for instance, Diamond neglects to mention the unintentional introduction of rats, a species whose voracious appetite for palm nuts may have played a role in the decimation of the island's ecology. Diamond blames human volition and short-sightedness when the underlying factors may be more complex and uncertain.

If we want a clear-cut parable, perhaps we can think of Céide Fields – apparently peacefully inhabited over centuries, before ecological change played an enormous role in bringing its way of life to an end. As has happened on every inhabited landmass, farmers arrived and cut down existing forests to make room for their precious domesticates. This exposed the area's soils which, given the intense rainfall characteristic of this corner of Europe, became leached and acidic. Ultimately abandoned, blanket bog would swallow up the remains of the community, leaving no visible trace that it had ever been there. Trees would never re-establish. This community of early Irish inhabitants left only two things behind: stone walls buried under blanket bog which hid what may be the earliest known field systems in Europe, and a landscape that would never be the same, even millennia later.

The collision

It's 1950. Having set off from RAF Aldergrove in Belfast, a World War II-era Halifax bomber was conducting a survey down the west coast of Ireland. Completing its task somewhere off the coast of Kerry, the craft returned north, flying at 1,800 feet, when heavy fog came in off the Atlantic. The navigator became disoriented, believing they were 148 miles further south than they actually were. The plane crashed into some of Europe's highest sea cliffs, where a mountain called Croaghaun (Cruachán, translating as 'little stack') rears out of the sea on Achill's coast. Locals thought the noise was an almighty crack of thunder. All eight crewmen on board perished, and today, all that's left at the site are the plane's engines, too large to be removed from this mushy, treacherous terrain.

This is a different wreck from either Céide or the Henge, invoking an entirely different reading of decline: as unforeseen, rapid, inevitable. A complex machine soars through a cloud of ignorance, soon to be wrecked on the mountainside, detritus of the past. As worlds end, the weathered metallic remains of the Halifax on Achill are a reminder of that common story. The end, this narrative tells us, is a specific data point on the timeline of ruination. *The Day After Tomorrow*. One day life is normal, and the next we are bereft, amidst decaying machines. As in many a fictional portrayal of collapse, what remains are ruinscapes filled with incongruous civilised materials, no longer fit for use.

A walking guide suggests that I visit the remains of the crash, lying on the far west of the island. It seems that my trip is quickly turning into a tour of wreck and folly. Fog rolls in, however, and any possibility for a visit is ruled out.

The unknown

As Achill would show, again and again while I traversed its lonely beauty, we're always already amidst the ruins. Just a mile from Achill Henge, at the foot of the island's second-tallest peak, Slievemore (Sliabh Mór, 'big mountain'), sits the 'abandoned village' – a string of around 80 rectangular stone huts, roofless and long-since abandoned. Heinrich Böll, who would go on to win the Nobel prize for literature in 1972, visited and lived on Achill at various times in the 1950s and 1960s. Wounded in World War II, he wrote evocatively about the village in his *Irish Journal*:

> No bombed city, no artillery-raked village ever looked like this, for bombs and shells are nothing but extended tomahawks, battle-axes, maces, with which to smash, to hack to pieces, but here there is no trace of violence; in limitless patience time and the elements have eaten away everything not made of stone, and from the earth have sprouted cushions on which these bones lie like relics, cushions of moss and grass.

As you walk through the abandoned village, the cushioned outlines of 'lazy beds' become clear; a form of traditional potato cultivation using raised ridges to make the best out of this sodden landscape (sloping downhill, of course, to spirit away the infernal rain). The catastrophic Great Famine of the mid-19th century is the first thought which comes to mind to explain the village's abandonment. Even in Böll's time on Achill, however, more than half a century ago, there was confusion about what had happened to the place and its people. 'No-one could tell us exactly when and why the village had been abandoned', he wrote.

While the famine did bring utter desolation to Mayo, which was one of the worst-hit areas, it seems that the decline of this village can be attributed to more recent factors: rent dissatisfaction, land redistribution, emigration. Used for summer dwelling in some of Ireland's last transhumance agriculture, these eerie stone boxes appear to be the legacy of multiple abandonments, deserted and reinhabited at various points, an ebb and flow of possibility and collapse which continued right up to the 1930s. In the end, nobody appears sure of what occurred.

Suffocation

Today, ten years after the economic collapse, Achill remains at a crossroads. Each year, more people die on the island than are born. Even those babies christened there are often brought by their parents to keep a link with the place that is their familial and spiritual, if no longer actual, home. Where Achill workers used to migrate for work a few months a year – to Scotland, for instance, or elsewhere in Ireland – they now leave and never return. As with much of rural Ireland, a death spiral is in motion. The island's abandonment intensifies each year, a process most visible during these dark winter months. This is a self-fulfilling pattern of decline. People move out; pubs, shops and schools close; other people move out for lack of pubs, shops and schools; more crucial services close; repeat ad infinitum. Death delivers further death, a bad infinity. What use are beauty, cliffs and salty wind in 2019, when Facebook and Twitter are recruiting in Dublin, 180 miles to the east? This is the way things are ending at capitalism's periphery: social asphyxiation, a slow, prolonged death.

Writing about Paul Klee's artwork, *Angelus Novus*, the critic and philosopher Walter Benjamin noted:

> Where we perceive a chain of events, he sees one single catastrophe which keeps piling wreckage upon wreckage and hurls it in front of his feet. The angel would like to stay, awaken the dead, and make whole what has been smashed. But a storm is blowing from Paradise; it has got caught in his wings with such violence that the angel can no longer close them. The storm irresistibly propels him into the future to which his back is turned, while the pile of debris before him grows skyward. This storm is what we call progress.

When you live with progress, apocalypse pushes in on all sides. It breathes down your neck. We can sense it these days, perhaps more than ever, amidst plagues of heat and hurricanes and floods. Yet, visiting this remote and barren corner of Ireland, speaking to those who persist, told me something about the extended and overlapping times and places of human endings, of collapse and renewal. Only in the capital-H history books has life ever been a linearity of events. Endings are always beginnings too, with the etymology of 'apocalypse' residing in the Greek *apo-kaluptein*, to reveal or uncover. We need to make peace with the fact that our dominance will end, that all lifeways ultimately push up against barriers, albeit at different paces.

As the sage Irish saying goes, 'When God made time, he made plenty of it.' What is to be done in the time bestowed upon us? Fatalistically give in to our decline, and curse our stupidity? Or do we huddle together through the dark nights and move at dawn? Appreciating our ruins is crucial and the Henge seems more necessary than ever if we are to reach more humble points of renewal. Ten years after the contagion of global crisis tipped a house of cards in Ireland, so little appears to have been learned. Mayo's palimpsest shows that in spite of the clamour to keep things as they are – the clamour to keep the project of human domination on its tracks – endings, large or small, are the refrain of history. They are always coming. Böll, too, learned this cosmic lesson from his time on the island:

> ...the Atlantic persistently carries away piece by piece the Western bastion of Europe; rocks fall into the sea, soundlessly the bog streams carry the dark European soil out into the Atlantic; over the years, gently plashing, they smuggle whole fields out into the open sea, crumb by crumb.

Stuck out on the edge of the world, Achill is a testament.

Daniel Nakanishi-Chalwin

Persimmons and Mist

On autumn words in haiku

Whether language determines reality, or reality language, is a moot point; John Keats has definitively given us Autumn. Its exquisite richness and bounty, mellow fruitfulness and the last oozings of the cyder-press. These are images of such charm that even autumn here where I live in Japan, remote from moss'd cottage-trees and hilly bourns, becomes refracted through them. There is the gentleness of the air after the fierce sun and relentless humidity of the summer; the succession of soft-dying days that prompts a withdrawal of chlorophyll – although this does not end a leaf's conspiracy with light. Rather, it is as if each gingko tree is now laden with a golden host of roosting butterflies, while the distant mountains smoulder with embers that live or die as the cloud cover shifts. Cherry leaves blush orange-rose, then drop like shivers of rust, old bloodstains; and all the tallow trees wear tongues of flame. At night, these visual signals convert to sound, to the bright stridulation of a million crickets. Transmissions that become persimmons hanging on bare branches, Belisha-orange in the thickening mist, the dying synapses of some great brain, as the insects fall silent one by one…

Stop! As Russell Hoban once put it, 'Let it be, you're wording it to death.'[1] Perhaps part of the difficulty is that autumn is not a stable condition so much as a dynamic process of transformation. Any description can therefore only ever be provisional. Words may proliferate, but totality remains elusive. Too much is not enough. So, try this instead:

山くれて	*Yama kurete*	The mountain grows darker,
紅葉の朱を	*momiji no ake o*	Taking the scarlet
うばひけり	*ubaikeri*	From the autumn leaves.[2]

– Buson

That's more like it. Three lines and 17 syllables in the original Japanese. The essence of those astonishing light effects without all that laborious phrase-making. It is not, however, simply its brevity that imbues a haiku with such power, with a vivid directness that seems to build something so massive in the mind. In addition to its 5–7–5 syllable scheme, each is formally required to contain a *kigo* or seasonally specific word. These include plants or animals (either in season or somehow more apparent in the human realm), meteorological or celestial phenomena more readily observable at that time of year, and traditional practices or their associated objects. Here are some examples for Autumn. The list is by no means exhaustive:

Red leaves (typically maple), yellow leaves (typically ginkgo), rowan, chrysanthemum, hardy begonia, bush clover, Japanese pampas grass, cluster amaryllis, sweet osmanthus, wolfsbane, rose mallow, rose balsam, morning glory, gentian, buckwheat flower, balloon flower, dayflower, burnet, ivy, kudzu, harlequin glorybower.

Persimmon, peach, watermelon, fig, millet, loofah, kumquat, pumpkin, sweet potato, taro, burdock root, acorn, Chinese quince, black-eyed bean, ginkgo nut, radish sprout, camellia fruit, chestnut and chestnut gathering, various species of mushroom (matsutake, shiitake, shimeji etc.) and mushrooming.

Salmon, Pacific saury, cutlassfish, sculpin, goby, sea bass, sardine, deer (particularly its mating call), wild boar, wild goose, woodpecker, quail, bull-headed shrike, Daurian redstart, snipe, dusky thrush, white-cheeked starling, brown-eared bulbul, wagtail, siskin, jay, praying mantis, mayfly, dragonfly, grasshopper, locust, various species of singing cricket, insect cage.

Typhoon, mackerel sky, the Milky Way, shooting star.

Thatch cutting, bamboo felling, tobacco leaf drying, *sake* tasting, sumō wrestling, rice harvesting, scarecrow, bird clapper, fulling block.

There are also phenomena that may occur in other seasons, but that somehow come into their own in the autumn, only then revealing their true character:

Mist, dew, the moon and moon-viewing, lightning ('thunder' is a summer season word).

Some kigo are especially evocative. *Hikoishi* means 'longing for fire', a perfect description of late autumn. *Sōkō*, literally 'frost fall', is an old name for the 23rd or 24th of October, when frost was said to form for the first time. Even apparently straightforward terms, however, are dense with cultural and historical associations. The origin of *aki no kure*, or 'autumn evening', can be traced far back beyond the history of haiku to at least the beginning of the 11th century. In her *Pillow Book*, a kind of private journal often recording profound aesthetic insights, Sei Shōnagon identified it as the quintessentially autumnal time of day, when the high skies and slowly failing light become suffused with pathos and the pull of home. Similarly, wild geese have been a common motif in all forms of Japanese poetry since the 8th century. Their arrival signalled the deepening of autumn, the growing desolation of the land. Their calls at night, resounding in the clear air, were held to be particularly moving.

病雁の	*Yamukari no*	a sick goose
夜寒に落ちて	*yosamu ni ochite*	falling into the night's coldness
旅寝かな	*tabine kana*	sleep on a journey.[3]

– Bashō

The loneliness of the poet on his travels intermingles with the weak cries of the animal – and with a thousand years of poetic sensibility. It is an example of how a haiku can create its own space from a single scene or moment, often as private and self-sufficient as a Joseph Cornell box construction, while simultaneously drawing on the power of shared experience encoded in its season word to imply the universal. It is the macro in the micro. Human perception melded with the other-than-human. The poetic rooted in the material world.

マンホール	*Manhōru*	When I stepped on a manhole
踏めば音して	*fumeba oto shite*	It made a noise –
秋の暮	*aki no kure*	Autumn evening.[4]

– Ikeda Shūsui

No mere inert signifiers, kigo have therefore altered over time, keeping pace with changing customs and lifestyles. Some more recent coinages for Autumn include: school sports day; the 1st of September (the anniversary of the Great Kantō earthquake of 1923); olives; pears; cosmos and *Dahlia imperialis* (both ornamental flowers originating in Mexico). Other words have completely lost their currency. A *kinuta* or 'fulling block' was used for pounding cloth by hand in order to soften the fibres and elicit a sheen, a defunct practice in industrialised Japan. *Kotori-gari* ('small bird hunting') referred to the catching of migratory species from continental Asia using fine nets or birdlime – techniques now outlawed. Good news for waxwings and thrushes, certainly, but yet a further distancing of omnivorous humans from some of the messy truths of existence. Ignore the gore and give it to us shrink-wrapped.

Indeed, these sterilising, flattening effects of modernity and globalisation are potentially lethal for an art form as attuned to seasonality as haiku. Advances in agriculture have extended the growing season for watermelons far into the summer months; so much so that it would be counter-intuitive for Japanese people to consider them an autumn fruit any more. Turnip and radish sprouts are cultivated year-round on a massive scale using plastic tubs and hydroponics, safely sealed off from the vagaries of the weather, while pumpkins imported from the Southern Hemisphere adorn supermarket shelves in April. And then, exacerbating all this relatively normalised topsy-turviness, there is modernity's most pernicious achievement – environmental collapse.

In part due to over-hunting, the wild goose population has dwindled and is now confined to northern Japan. The locust – a crop pest on the one hand, a once ready source of extra protein on the other – has been decimated by agrochemicals, which have further combined with the effects of land reclamation to endanger delicate wetland areas, putting a number of dragonfly species at risk of extinction. Everywhere systems run out of kilter. I have lived in the same city for the last ten years and have seen typhoons become more destructive and unpredictable. The 2018 season included one bizarre storm, Jongdari, which veered off its initially conventional course to execute a U-turn before making landfall. Other ruptures are less dramatic, but equally unsettling. Should that summer cicada still be singing in autumn, its quivering body matching the shimmering of the air? In fact, why is it still so damn hot? Why has the cool breeze of autumn been replaced by a second skin of sweat? Why are the four seasons rapidly collapsing into two – summer and other-than-summer? Why do haiku resemble pictures of a gone world? Why the schism between language and reality?

Of course, it is never a good idea to fetishise any art form as the ultimate encapsulator of reality. Even the concise and clear-eyed haiku can succumb to idealism, like a suspiciously flattering portrait of a monarch. The season word *risshū* is a case in point. Meaning 'the start of autumn', it marks the official moment when the weather begins to shift, the temperature drops and the poignant dying back of the earth commences. The only problem is, it currently falls on the 7th or 8th of August, the sweatiest, most draining phase of the summer (climate change notwithstanding). The cause is an ancient act of self-deception. Poetry culture in Japan, based around the old imperial capital of Kyoto, has traditionally modelled itself on that of China, from where it took the practice of dividing the year into four, with its fixed dates. Unfortunately, the seasons in China's literary heartland, around Chang'an and Luoyang on the Yellow River, are approximately a month further advanced than in Kyoto. Japan's intelligentsia thus resorted to some torturous reasoning to maintain their literary fiction: risshū *is the threshold beyond which it cannot become any hotter, when only the most sensitive souls can detect the subtly cooling air and the sweet sadness of autumn…*

So, language fails again. Even the focussed gaze of the haiku does not always capture truthfully the complexity of the world. These are words as dead leaves. Beautiful. Brittle. Faded.

I have always considered Dark Mountain a project for an autumnal age, when loss and beauty co-exist and winter threatens. Now, after a decade of worsening crises, we find ourselves inescapably in late autumn, the mist beginning to swallow the persimmons, the lights going out one by one. More than ever, we need uncivilised writing – the antidote to language as solipsistic word game, trapped in the maze of its own delusion. This is not the time for citadels of literature, for great linguistic edifices. We must pack our tentative words with as much power as the kigo in the most insightful haiku, tiny parts of tiny poems. We must re-entangle our language with the real, with the Earth as it is, make it as intense as those bright orange persimmons on the verge of disappearance.

Perhaps not dying synapses, after all.

Beacons.

As the *Dark Mountain Manifesto* proclaimed:

> Our words will be elemental.

Or, as Kobayashi Issa put it in 1814:

青空に	*Aozora ni*	In the clear blue sky
指で字をかく	*yubi de ji o kaku*	I write with my finger
秋の暮	*aki no kure*	This autumn evening.[5]

Notes

1. Hoban, R. *The Medusa Frequency*, Bloomsbury, 2002, p. 96
2. Translation by Blyth, R.H. *Haiku: Volume 4, Autumn – Winter*, Hokuseido Press, 1982, p. 1083
3. Translation by Reichhold, J. *Basho: The Complete Haiku*, Kodansha Intl, 2008, p. 169
4. Included in *Haiku Saijiki – Aki [Haiku Seasonal Glossary – Autumn]*, Kadokawa Shoten, 5th edition, 2018, p. 25. Translation my own.
5. Translation my own.

Em Strang

Horse-Man at Crotha Bothy

Beloved,

First light, fire, tea. I strip-wash at the sink as the moon goes down behind one hill and the sun rises over another. I stand outside on the deck at just after 6am and the whole glen is silent, utterly soundless, except for the first calls of small birds and the flowing burn. No wind. The trees are motionless.

I wish never to forget – this is where we come from and return to, at last.

Margaret Elphinstone

Rewilding Who We Are

Ideology feels like reality when you live inside it. It's 'normal' for those of us in the Global North to operate inside a culture which is on a suicidal collision course with the needs of the planet. The evidence for climate change, species extinction and environmental collapse escalates every day, yet we still observe how most people, particularly those who think they govern the rest of us, seem not to care; or, if they do, make almost no attempt to change things. It seems inexplicable, until one examines the ideology which enthrals our culture. Until we learn to think beyond redundant ideologies, we actually cannot act differently.

We live in a world of constructed oppositions: in almost every known language, things are defined by what they are not: nature/culture, wild/tame, male/female, good/evil and so on. I doubt whether the other creatures who share our planet think in such binary oppositions. Does a dog who is warm and dry think 'not cold and wet'? Or does she just revel in the moment as it is? No-one could regret our facility with language, but it comes at a price. Once we can speak, we are partially separated from our experience, aware of alternative possibilities, never wholly present in what is. Languages are also full of tenses. The past is over and done with; the future is permanently a possibility just over the horizon. The present is obscured by regret and disappointment about the past and plans and objectives for the future. If faced with global catastrophe, our minds rush to the past – where we can safely put the blame – and the future, which is the place where we keep our solutions. The place in the middle – the one we are in right here, right now – gets squeezed out, which is a pity, because it's the only place where we can actually do anything.

The Hopi people of North America have a story explaining how we became separated through our oppositional language. The Hopi story doesn't feature a garden, or a serpent, or an apple, but, like the story in Judeo-Christian cultures, there's an opposition at the heart of it, which bears some relation to the Genesis story about gaining the knowledge of good/evil. The Hopi story goes like this: The Mockingbird chattered and talked, and People listened and copied him. Through all this talk, the Mockingbird persuaded the People that they were different from everyone else. Mockingbird pointed out that they wore clothes and spoke languages, and knew about the spirits. Once the People were convinced that they were different, the Animals became afraid of them and avoided them. People even started avoiding each other, and when they did meet, they fought and sometimes even killed each other. Once People start thinking they are different, it is not only other species that become the alienated Other, it's also other humans who are not of their tribe. Xenophobia becomes part of the same package.

Once we start to coin words like 'nature', 'wild' and 'wilderness', we express a further sense of dislocation. These strange words show us that we're not fully inhabiting the planet out of which we evolved, of which we are an integral part. In the presence of non-human landscapes and non-human lives, *present* is exactly what we're not. When we come anywhere close to being present, we feel it as a flash of illumination, a blinding revelation. We become aware of something larger than self, an intensity of feeling – perhaps joyous, perhaps painful – in which we feel wholly alive. This is what it is like, just for a moment, to know who and where you are, to belong.

Such moments can happen to anyone, anywhere; there is no hierarchy and no-one is excluded. No-one's experience is invalid or unimportant. The connection between human beings and the living world around us is integral to our being – awareness of connection is the full meaning of being alive. As such, it is egalitarian in ways for which our prevailing ideology has no concept. Instead, we recognise 'experts' who specialise in 'nature' in their writing, art or science. The binary opposite of these experts is the ignorant masses who, steeped in ignorance and irresponsibility, crowd together in our doomed cities. If we're going to address what it really means to be re-connected, we have to free ourselves from this kind of thinking altogether, which smacks alarmingly of older oppositions: good/bad, saved/damned, rich/poor.

Perhaps there are other sentient beings inhabiting this planet who are aware of this connectedness all the time. The moments that seem to change our world, in which it feels like we'll never see things in quite the same way again, may simply *be* their world. For them, it all just *is*. These other beings don't have language as we understand it, so we have no idea what they're experiencing. Our ability to conceptualise and communicate – such great gifts – can also be a poisoned chalice. Separation from the living world around us means that we forget to listen to these other lives, which may embody something vital which we have lost.

What do these curious cultural constructions, 'nature' and 'wild', say about those of us who use them? Is there any way around them, any way back to where we came from?

As long as they stand as an opposition, as something Other than the domesticated culture to which we belong, we define such terms as something out there which we are not. Somewhere in our own childhood, and in our human evolution, we began to see the living world around us as something outside ourselves. If we are the subject, then the rest of the living world becomes merely the object of our gaze. Nature and wildness can be used to gratify our senses, or exploit what we call its resources, but we are not part of it. We have lost touch.

But we are animals; our place is in the whole intricate web of life on Earth. If we lose that place, we lose ourselves. There is nowhere else for us to be, and our species doesn't make any sense by itself. Like all other animals, we breathe, eat, grow, excrete, sense, move, reproduce, and we're made of the same stuff. As soon as we stop doing these things, we die and get recycled, like everything else. Without air, without the Earth and the things that grow on it, without water and sunlight, we don't exist. There is nothing embodied in us that is not part of the whole, and that includes our thoughts, our dreams, our stories, our sciences, our cities, our souls and indeed every concept we have ever formulated.

Rewilding who we are is about re-making these lost connections and listening to the lives which we've discounted for so long. We have made more of those lives extinct during my lifetime than had disappeared from the Earth since the dinosaurs. If we're incapable of adapting, then in Darwinian terms, we should become extinct too. The most enduring legacy we would leave would be radioactive air, extinct species and plastic seas. The damage of our other depredations would repair itself quite quickly. In this lies a sort of hope.

But, like other species, we're programmed to survive and reproduce at all costs. I would like to be part of that survival too. If we don't want our story to end like this, how can we adapt? I don't believe we have it in ourselves to do so. As climate change and pollution escalate, it becomes ever clearer that our culture is not able to overcome its destructive tendencies, however hard some individuals try to change things. We cannot change direction all by ourselves. We need help. It is just possible, even at this eleventh hour, that we could find it. We're not alone. The other lives which share our planet have been treated for too long merely as either material resources or undesirable competitors. There is an exchange in *The Tao of Pooh*, by Benjamin Hoff, that goes like this:

> 'Lots of people talk to Animals,' said Pooh.
> 'Maybe, but...'
> 'Not very many listen though,' he said.
> 'That's the problem'.

Hunters and gatherers (of the indigenous sort, not modern trophy hunters) have to observe and understand these living beings around them; they have to know what the plants and animals are like, and what they'll do. They have to listen, and their stories too are about listening. People learned what life meant from the spirits, or the animals, which is how they know the stories are true. The stories answer the perennial questions that humans ask: What are we doing here? What do our lives mean? How will it all end? The stories are about the beginning and end of all things, and usually animals and plants are the prime movers in the narrative. The stories are also about what it means for a person to journey through life, and what other beings – animals, plants, spirits – will help her along her way.

Significantly, the only place in a post-industrial world where the animals retain their significance in story is in narratives for young children. Becoming an adult is, in our culture, largely about separating oneself from the beings around us, becoming disconnected. Such a notion of maturity is wholly unlike, for example, the Australian Aboriginal Dreamtime, which is about connection with other beings. In recent editions of the Oxford Children's Dictionary, words about the natural world were deleted. As Robert Macfarlane states eloquently in the introduction to *The Lost Words*, by depriving our children of words for other lives, we make these other lives invisible, linguistically non-existent.

Because we have language, knowledge and self-consciousness, we do appear to be unique among animals. Like every other living being, we live on energy from the sun, which we can access by consuming other plants and animals. However, unlike the other living beings (so far as we can tell), we're aware of ourselves taking other lives in order to feed our own. A bargain only works if both sides treat each other with respect, and hunter-gatherer societies take care to maintain the dialogue between People and Animals, Hunter and Hunted. But the more separated a human culture becomes from the world around it, the less respectful it is towards other beings. Those who feel the connection most – who might have become shamans in a hunter-gatherer culture – cannot bear what we do. Think, for example, of the 19th-century poet John Clare, who felt so strongly connected to the English countryside that its despoliation by advancing industrialisation drove him finally into a mental asylum. 'Nature' was not a backdrop for him, or a mirror, or a resource, it was life itself, and to be alive was to be connected to the whole:

All nature has a feeling: woods, fields, brooks
Are life eternal: and in silence they
Speak happiness beyond the reach of books;
There's nothing mortal in them; their decay
Is the green life of change; to pass away
And come again in blooms revivified.
Its birth was heaven, eternal is its stay,
And with the sun and moon shall still abide
Beneath their day and night and heaven wide.

It is possible that our place in this natural cycle is nearly at an end. Perhaps we can accept this, if we drop our notions of linear time. In our post-Einsteinian world, these are already obsolete among storytellers – both artists and scientists. All those stories about the first cow, or the first ash tree, or the first turtle – with which our living world began – are cyclic. They circle through days and seasons and aeons of life until they reach the end of all things, when Fenris the Wolf appears, or Black Rain falls, or our Earth dies giving birth to a cosmic egg, or the World Serpent swallows up the sun. There's going to be an ending, of course. One day, according to the current story, the sun will explode and turn into a black hole. There will have been many other endings by then.

Is the present moment any the less valid for possibly being near the end of our cycle? I would like my grandchildren to live long and happy lives. I'd also like them never to suffer, which of course isn't possible. I can't do anything about that. But today I can read my youngest granddaughter a poem out of *The Lost Words* and she'll enjoy that, we'll be happy, and she'll understand better who and where she is. The only place where I can make anything happen is here and now. This doesn't mean I don't care about where we're going, or that I won't do anything about it. I say 'where we're going', not 'the future'. 'The future' is an abstract noun; I can't get anywhere near it. 'Where we're going' is a pronoun and an active verb; it is what we're doing right now. In the here and now, we can do things, like stop, turn, look, listen, change direction – the things we were taught to do in order to cross the road. There are many difficult crossings in front of us, now we find ourselves going the other way.

If we listen to what the plants and animals are telling us, we might – whatever happens – find stories which fit our times better. The stories we currently tell ourselves about control and crisis management are not helping us. Their hero is isolated, terrified and in an increasing state of panic. This hero encounters wildfires in California, floods in Bangladesh, Arctic heatwaves and dead coral reefs, and tries frantically to delete them from the script. Unlike Taliesin, the bard who drank from the cauldron of wisdom and heard the birds and animals speak, this hero has manically stopped his ears to what the land and the animals are saying.

This is what Taliesin said about himself, after he had become many animals in all the elements:

> I was in many shapes before I was released:
> I was a slender, enchanted sword...
> I was rain-drops in the air, I was stars' beam;
> I was a word in letters, I was a book in origin;
> I was lanterns of light for a year and a half;
> I was a bridge that stretched over sixty estuaries;
> I was a path, I was an eagle, I was a coracle in seas.

This is what it is to be connected. This hero is at one with the living world around him. He can be himself without drawing boundaries around himself and making himself separate. Our hunter-gatherer ancestors knew they had to cross these separating boundaries in order to survive. It is what we have to do too. Sometimes we have done it, when we experience that flash of illumination, that momentary sense of connection with all life. As far as we know, we are the only animals who can conceive taking on other shapes and imagine what it's like to be somebody else. Possibly, even, that is what our imaginations are *for*. Our ability to conceptualise needn't be just an evolutionary disaster. It has been a successful genetic adaptation, in that – like cockroaches and cancer cells – we have proliferated remarkably. But what a transformation it would be if we re-forged it into a story of empathy and recognition.

Changing our whole ideology may seem like too slow a process to address the crisis we are facing, but the speed of response is up to us: it can indeed be slow or it can be instant, in this present moment. The polar ice is melting *now.* Sea animals are being choked with microplastics *now*. If you could transform into a turtle *now*, or a polar bear, or a coral atoll, there would be things our society takes for granted which you could never bring yourself to do again. You would be empowered by the wisdom you had gained from listening to those other lives. Because you were intrinsically part of these other lives, you would cast fear and embarrassment aside and stand up for them. You would think of ways, even if it killed you, which it might.

I think there is a way. It starts with acts of imagination and empathy. It starts with renewing the stories about connection, and the narrative goes on from there. This adaptation of an old story may come quite near the end of the human cycle. It may be the beginning of a new chapter. Either way, the hero of this new story will know, here and now, what she must do.

Vinay Gupta

Damn the Day Jobs

It is 50°C in India today, not out in the wilderness, but in the city of Churu. It's probably even hotter in the places without thermometers.

In the early days, at the festivals, Dark Mountain always struck me as very English – very real ale and folk music. The thing that it was interested in preserving was the village of English mythic imagination, a place of rosy-cheeked apples and babies, between John Barleycorn and John Bull, middle England. The settings, the people, the songs, and always the ale. It was a microcosm of a particular place and time, a rich current of pastoralism mounting its literary defence against the downstream consequences of these dark satanic mills. That was its strength, and its greatest weakness. As it expanded globally, it remained about where you were, and who you were – the triumph of the personal and parochial over the political and global.

The point I tried to impress, again and again, is that global warming and all the rest of it disproportionately affect the poor first, and the poor are not rural white farmers, but teeming masses in scorching Asian and African and (Latin) American cities, eking out a living. The carbon crisis is directly tied to the fruits of colonialism: mostly-white nations paralysed the global negotiations by insisting that everybody should tighten their carbon belts by 20%, regardless of their current malnutrition levels. The voices which say 'every human being, including historic human beings, has an equal right to emit carbon' didn't get much of a hearing. Neither did the people toting their solar panels or talking about geoengineering.

In those days, I was the court jester. I'd come from a heavy defence environment in America, helping organise the Pentagon's STAR-TIDES project on collaborative approaches to crisis response, including climate refugees. I'd worked on pandemic flu, nuclear terrorism, genocide. That was hard material to process. I never had access to the classified planning; my role was to think about things in the open, in civil-military networks particularly, so I'd always been outside of the wire, peering in, trying to understand if the situation was under control. It wasn't. Not even close.

So I felt my responsibilities pretty keenly in those days, and it took a few years of goofing around to blow off steam and return to a more normal equilibrium as my ties to the defence world thinned out. The phase of my life where I wore a skull jacket and carried business cards that said 'I don't get out of bed for less than 1% mortality' concealed a simple, basic truth: I felt myself alone with the worst problems in the world, because when I got out the spreadsheet and started calculating death tolls, nobody was willing to carry the other end of the plank. Not civilian, not military. Nobody.

There was a time when I was probably the most educated human on earth in the domains of mass mortality and human extinction scenarios, and what to do about them. It's pretty dark at the top of that particular mountain. There is not a lot of light, not even from flashlights, and there are few friends.

So I played jester for a while, then went back to work. I joined the Ethereum team, launching our carbon-belching, slow, inefficient, mostly-uncensorable, distributed, decentralised global computer. I did it because we need a global machine to track resources – carbon, steel, migrants across borders. We need that world computer's ninth-generation descendant to track every living blade of grass and bee, to tell us *for sure and immediately* whether neonicotinoid pesticides are killing the bees or not, and exactly who made how much money from however many deaths the climate chaos caused this month. We need accounting, to enforce accountability.

In America, the weather is so wet they can't plant much corn or soy this year. It is the first harbinger of famine. Maybe they'll pull through this year. One year soon, they won't, and food prices will rise, and the poor will do the starving, rioting, bleeding and dying.

Steve Wheeler

Full Circle

JUNE 2010. I've been at the first Uncivilisation gathering in Llangollen in North Wales for three days now, and I'm starting to grow frustrated. Surely I should feel differently? – like I am at home, that I have found my people. After a decade studying the collapse of civilisations, educating myself on ecology and economics and producing a PhD on that classic subject, Everything Ever All At Once, I ought to be thriving on the opportunity to finally have conversations with people who share my understanding of the world and our precarious place within it.

But I'm not, and I think I know why. It's the final day, it's sunny outside, and I feel like moving. Somehow, my truancy gathers collaborators, and I end up teaching an impromptu martial arts class outside on the grass. Nothing too challenging – just familiarising people with the sensation of blocking an arm as it comes towards you, introducing them to the idea that you can feel confident, comfortable even, in a situation of potential aggression and conflict. Much of my PhD research had involved a similar sort of truancy, training in the eccentric art of *Baguazhang* instead of preparing academic articles for publication.

The night before, I and the few people I'd known before arriving at Uncivilisation had eaten out in a pub that used to be a mill. As we sat overlooking the foam and chatter of the River Dee, one after another announced that they were leaving their jobs in London. I'm pretty sure it wasn't just the 'Dark Mountain Effect', or the giddiness of being out of the city; they'd been planning their departures for a while. But I found myself saying 'Me too!' – and realising, with a shock, that I meant it. Eighteen months earlier I'd taken a job ineffectually reprimanding the British newspaper industry, partly to demonstrate to myself that I'd been avoiding the nine-to-five for good reason and not purely out of cowardice or immaturity. But that purpose had been served, and it felt like those 18 months had stolen years of my life and health. It was time to move again.

*

Stop. Don't move a muscle. Whatever posture you find yourself in, whatever awkward position – even if your coffee cup is halfway to your mouth – stay frozen like that. Now slowly let your attention percolate through the whole of your body, listening for temperature, pressure, sensation, emotion. Whatever you find there, let it be. If you become aware of a particular pattern of tension or pain; if you are suddenly uncomfortably aware of fullness, heat, itching or tiredness; if you feel the first tricklings of grief, or anger, or impatience; don't try to change it, don't be tempted to shift your position or tense or relax your muscles. Just observe. And now notice, too, the rhythmic pulse of your breath moving through this pattern of sensations. Note if it feels shallow, or short, or tight, or rough – but don't try to change the breath either.

*

We think we know what time is, but the linear time we know from the 'outside' – clock time, historical time, progressing forward into the future in orderly, unidirectional fashion like a train gliding smoothly along the tracks – is nothing like as universal as we assume, even in our own lives. The Greeks, among others, imagined themselves moving backwards into time, since the past was visible and the future was not. Indigenous peoples often lack any abstract term for 'time' at all, inhabiting a subjective realm where time is dilatory, uncountable, entangled with space and movement and the natural cycles of the wider environment. There seems to be a close relationship between a lack of concern for the 'passage' of time and an intensity of experience in the present moment, which lends itself to an animistic understanding of the world. We can only imagine what it must be like to live with such an unwavering degree of presence – those still left to tell us speak of the sacredness of all being, of the creation of the world being enacted in every moment.

The first civilisations stepped only a few paces away from this eternal present. In Sumer, Egypt, India and Olmec Mesoamerica, sacred calendars nested multiple repeating cycles of time, marked by a pattern of festival days. Although the newly civilised inhabitants were called upon to exercise the deferral of pleasure, to attend to abstractions with effortful attention, the festivals regularly returned them to the 'time of origins', reimmersing the self in the lost plenitude of Being. Each festival in the liturgical calendar of the year was at once a kind of pressure valve, a practical means of releasing the tensions of civilised life, and a gap in the flow of cyclical time through which sacred time, eternity, could leak back through into the profane world.

The linear idea of time was just a further progression from this, where the smaller, repeating arcs away from Being were condensed into a single, all-encompassing span. Oswald Spengler talks of the 'cavern' as the defining temporal motif of the Levantine cultures – historical time held within the vault of the timeless, a space of linear duration stretched open in the intensity of eternal Being. Within this cavern-space the beginning and end of time are poised somewhere between cyclical and linear consciousness: not quite an instantaneous beginning and end, nor unfolding in strict historical time, but the fabric of space-time curving round at the edges of the cavern, mixing the chronological and the mythic, the linear and the eternal.

There is a death-fear at the heart of this new form of consciousness – stepping outside the charmed circle of animism leads to a new sense of vulnerability, of being a lonely, isolated 'I' amid a threatening world. Some say the seeds were planted around 4000 BC, when reductions in rainfall and the subsequent desertification of North Africa and the Near East disrupted the traditional, cyclical patterns of living and demanded a more hostile and warlike form of society. From this came the growth of the first patrist, imperialist civilisations. The assumption of scarcity and competition led to a more instrumentalist and future-oriented mindset, more brutal patterns of child-rearing, a hostile attitude towards physical pleasure, and a loss of respect for women, animals and the natural world.

For whatever reason, this fear of the end of one's own mortal span was mirrored by the anticipation of the end of historical time itself: the Apocalypse. Far from simply being an arbitrary bookend to an infinite unfolding of time, the Apocalypse is the final closure of time's parabola – the debt becoming due, the elastic space of linearity snapping shut. It immerses us back in the realm of mythic undifferentiation from which we were exiled and, as such, it is something that we both fear and desire – the End of Days, but also the Day of Judgement, when all the sacrifices made by living in linear time will be accounted for and rewarded. In comparison to this anticipated redemption, the profane world comes to seem petty and unimportant – a mere theatre of religious performance in which, so long as it serves the core values of the apocalyptic mythos, any degree of violence and inhumanity can be justified.

*

AUGUST 2013. It is the Sunday morning of the final Uncivilisation Festival in Hampshire in southern England. I am leading a workshop called 'Full Circle'. A group of humans are sitting in a ring, looking at me, expecting me to know what to do next.

For the last three years, since we moved the festival here to the more homespun surroundings of the Sustainability Centre, I have led workshops on what I am coming to call 'Human Rewilding'. This year, I took on the job of organising an entire 'Rewilding Academy' of embodied activities, featuring sensory immersion, barefoot running, candlelit midnight yoga, and much else – a job made more difficult by my brother's decision to have his wedding on the weekend of the festival, and to choose me as best man.

The evening before, having delivered my speech and said my goodbyes, I got changed in the pub car park and aquaplaned down the M23 to conduct the Saturday night 'ritual' in Hampshire. The rain was easing off just as I arrived, and I found the camp a Marie Celeste: quiet, seemingly unpopulated, the dark heavy with mist, until finally I turned a corner to stumble upon a yellow glow of faces, rapt in a singer's performance. After the ritual – fire, words, gestures, a circle of people looking at me, expecting me to know what to do next – a strange, celebratory, spontaneous game of call and response emerged, running into the small hours.

This morning, we're talking about how tribal peoples sit in circles facing each other, and how that differs from the rectilinear layouts of classrooms, parliaments and corporate meetings. My friend Goia is part of the circle, and the conversation prompts him to share something about his time practicing the martial art *capoeira*, where the two *capoeiristas* 'play' in a circle of people: 'It's never occurred to me before,' he says, 'but all that time spent sitting with humans to either side of you has a natural effect on your perception; it makes you more lateral, more democratic, less likely to want to assert your own narrow viewpoint onto the group.'

Another of the participants – an older, neatly bearded gentleman – tells us of how his wristwatch had somehow gone missing during the Happenings of the night before; and how he had found it again, mysteriously, right next to him when he'd woken in his tent this morning. Somehow, symbolically, it seemed we had slipped the bonds of ordinary time last night and re-entered the timeless realm of carnival.

*

Focus your eyes on a point a good distance away. Take a deep breath, and let it go. Then slowly, gently, shift your attention to your peripheral vision. Become aware of the full width of your visual field. Try to soften the feeling in your eyes, as if looking kindly at something you love. Go back and forth between the central focus and the wider field a few times – slowly, always slowly! Now, look once more at the point in front of you. Breath in, and tense every muscle in your body. Then let it all go – release the breath, let your muscles relax, and allow your eyes to soften into the wider view. Then wiggle your toes. Listen to any reactions – physical, mental, emotional – without judgement.

*

Our own European civilisation evolved the 'alienation' of linear time yet further. In the early centuries of the last millennium, most of the inhabitants of Europe still lived in a largely cyclical world. Despite the hardships of mediaeval life, a worker's day was marked by long breaks to eat and sleep, and up to a third of the year was taken up with religious festivals and holidays. Many of these were Christianised versions of older pagan festivities: Carnival, Fastnacht, Mardi Gras,

The Feast of Fools – their licentiousness and Saturnalian inversions of authority affording some relief from the constrictions of feudal hierarchy and linear time.

At that time, the idea of Apocalypse remained a literal and material expectation; a promise of delayed gratification without which the feudal social structure, and the justificatory mechanisms of religion that enabled it, would not have been possible. There were dangers to this, of course – a populace expecting release from the bondage of time was tempted, on occasion, to give Providence a helping hand, and the mediaeval ages were marked by a succession of millenarian movements, rebellions and revolts.

But then things changed. As a larger proportion of the population was drawn up into linear time, the immanent – and imminent – Apocalypse was swept under the metaphysical carpet, replaced by ideas of earthly Utopia, which themselves gave way to the more abstract temporal notion of Progress. The pattern was matched by changes in Christian theology. The immanent Creator, manifesting the universe in every moment, withdrew to a remote past, a *Deus absconditus* that had set the universe into initial motion but taken no further part in its operation. By Newton's time, it was possible to speak of a 'clockwork universe', a material mechanism evacuated of numinosity and meaning.

This shift in perspective was both created and exacerbated by technological change. It was a cultural imperative that placed clocks on the church towers of Europe from the 14th century on: they initially served little practical purpose, being rather an embodiment of the metaphysical ideal of objective time. Slowly, however, society began to be organised around these inorganic divisions of duration. Where once life had been shaped by attendance to organic rhythms and needs, it began to be regulated by the numbers on the clock face. By the late 16th century, these streams of technology, theology and psychology were merging in the rigid scheduling of whole communities: when persecuted Huguenot clockmakers fled to Geneva, they found there a perfect marriage with the austere Calvinist theocracy. The result was not only the birth of the Swiss clock industry, but the creation of a whole set of temporal values centred around productivity, punctuality and the suppression of pleasure and spontaneity – the eradication of the last vestiges of Carnival.

As improved chronometric technology allowed the calculation of longitude, these values were spread around the globe on the spear point of European conquest. In Ming Dynasty China, Jesuit missionaries used the obsession with Western clocks as one tool to gain favour in the country. Imperial administrators concerned themselves with the need to impose clock time on indigenous populations – at home as well as abroad. Time itself became the battleground of ideology: as the industrial world took shape, a sense of guilt around time, speed and punctuality needed to be inculcated, and the workers were plied with sugar, tea and coffee – the stimulants of Empire – to ensure they could keep up with the new industrialised pace. Without their own source of 'authoritative' time, they were often exploited by factory owners, who would rig clocks to extend the work day; and, when workers in the 19th century took action for a reduced work day, it was often the clock above the factory gates that would be the first thing to be destroyed.

The final ties with subjective, local time began to be cut. With the increased speed afforded by railway travel, there arose a need for a single coordinated time imposed by a central authority, rather than being calculated from the zenith of the sun in each locality. By the mid-20th century, time zones encircled the world in a grid of standardised chronology, organic, human-scale time only a dim memory to a few. The simple pleasures of physical contentment were driven out by the demands of industrial scheduling – the mechanisation of life drained 'everyday' time of inherent meaning. Only the idea of Progress – the eternal present exiled to the far end of time – held the ennui at bay; the suppressed energy of the Apocalyptic lurking just beneath its glib surface, wound up like the spring of a clock.

*

SEPTEMBER 2016. Someone had to be scheduled against David Abram. Set in the lush valley of Embercombe in Devon, 'Base Camp' is the first Dark Mountain festival for three years. We have managed to arrange for US author David Abram, a major influence on many people involved in the project, to speak as part of it. For many it is the much-anticipated highlight of the weekend.

It's quarter past 11 on Sunday morning. One of the key organisers has been delirious with fever in a yurt all weekend, several people went to hospital last night, and it doesn't look like anyone is turning up to my workshop. One of the two Swedish documentary makers who have been filming all weekend is shifting from foot to foot. 'I might just go up the hill for the beginning of David Abram,' he says. 'I will come back down in half an hour.' I don't think he will, but I don't blame him – the site is split between two main areas with a long, steep walk between them, and he has lugged his camera equipment up and down it dozens of times already over the last few days.

Somehow, in the course of six years, the number of attendees at my Rewilding workshops has gone from 50, to 15, to none. I breathe out and relax. It's OK. This doesn't have to be about me. In 'The People's Circle' – a quiet ring of grassy embankment at the bottom of the hill – it feels like the land is holding me. There's nowhere else I need to be. I start to run through some exercises from Baguazhang; if no-one else is here, I can still work on making my own body and mind more comfortable.

And then, in ones and twos, they arrive. 'I was going to go to David Abram,' the dozen or so latecomers sheepishly announce, 'but I'm just so full of words after this weekend, I needed to do something else.' After an hour or so of our lying on the grass, humming, listening to the bird-song, of moving fluidly in space around each other, of paying attention to the bare patterns of sensation in our bodies, we finish up the session and look around. Everyone seems different: relaxed, making soft but certain eye contact, breathing more fully and easily. Everyone looks like they have landed again in themselves; like they have remembered something.

*

> Lie on the ground – preferably somewhere soft; preferably somewhere grassy and sun-dappled. Take a deep breath, and let it go. Take another, and this time turn the exhalation into a long, slow hum. Keep your teeth apart, and see how much of your body you can make resonate with the vibration of the

hum. Keep humming with each exhalation, and begin to add movements: first, turning the head gently from side to side; then allow the shoulders to pick up from the ground as the head turns; then allow the arms to follow, moving however they want. Keep the body as relaxed as possible as you move. Try to cultivate the effortless feeling of yawning in your movements. If it feels possible, see if you can move onto your front, onto all fours, or even stand up with the same quality of movement. Then lie, breathing normally, on the ground, and pay attention to the sensations in your body.

*

All around us, we see a society determined to increase the velocity of living, to push further away from the natural rhythms of organic life, to fragment its attention with a multitude of distractions. The logic of speed, the ideology of Progress, and the Calvinist demand for a pleasureless, mechanical universe have wreaked untold devastation, threatening the very survival of human and more-than-human life on this planet.

What dreams and stories do we tell ourselves in times like this? On every bookshelf, from every screen, come images of world-ending destruction, of civilisational collapse: cities aflame, ground sundered, the lines and order of modernity shattered into chaos. Such images are born of fear, but also of deep, hidden desire: for the promised release, for the 'revealing' of the true world beyond time, for the redemption of Final Judgement.

When we anticipate an explosion, we hold our breath. When we are still, but expecting to suddenly move, we subtly tense our muscles. When we are anxious for the future, our minds race in an attempt to anticipate all possible hazards. The pattern of deferral of pleasure, of diminished emotional affect, the hypercognition that accompanies alienation from the body, and the hidden rigidity that comes from fearing – and desiring – the promised End: all this is present in the body of a human who has mistakenly internalised the logic of Apocalypse.

In Western society today, we see an epidemic of anxiety and

hypercognition, of people cut off from their own bodies and their own deeper capacity for feeling. Even when we try to correct the situation, rather than returning to the body – which would entail fully feeling the anxiety we have been trying so hard to avoid – we take every chance to climb back up the hill to the realm of abstract, cerebral analysis. We might even say that thought and feeling are opposed for many; the more we try to think our way out of the trap, the further alienated from bodily wisdom we become.

The crisis we face is unprecedented in scope and severity. But to react to it through the frame of Apocalypse would be a grave error, for that is the same template of fear, contraction and denial that has led us to this very climacteric. The solution to a pattern of fear cannot be found in cultivating more fear, just as the solution to an excess of 'thought-chatter' is never further thought-chatter. When we are told to panic, that this is an emergency, that we only have 11 years left to act, the deep logic of the Apocalyptic kicks in; numbing us from true feeling, separating us from participation with the living world, and paralysing us from engaging in effective action.

The solution, as so often, is so simple as to be largely overlooked. It is to reject the Apocalyptic constructs – the denial of festivity, the alienation from feeling, the tyranny of artificial time – and to return to simplicity itself: to the body, human community, natural rhythms, and the undiluted intensity of simply Being. Some might claim this is an abdication of responsibility at a time when swift action is needed. But to reject the mechanised timetable of haste and panic is to reconnect with the very thing we need most at this time. We have tried to take shortcuts to redemption before, and have only succeeded in reanimating the pathological values of the Apocalypse. Now, when things are most urgent, is precisely when we must learn once again how to slow down, to achieve nothing, to simply be. And, from that stillness, we may be able to remember who, and when, we are.

*

JUNE 2019. It's midnight. I am in the dining hall of a Steiner school in southern Sweden. Everyone else has gone to bed, but I am trying to finish this essay before the two-week meditation retreat begins tomorrow morning. In the absence of other humans, the ecological lighting system has shut down, sector by sector, until I am left typing in the dark. The irony of writing about slowing down and doing nothing against a tight deadline is not lost on me. I've been joking about how I'm about to write my piece on The Importance of Slowness – 'but I haven't quite got round to it yet' – for nine years now, and time has finally caught up with me.

No martial arts this summer: I've come full circle, to where movement has to give way to stillness. In a sense, it feels like I've been running on the spot for a decade, while watching my peers build families, careers, businesses. By the mainstream values of the society I live within, aside from a few published pieces in Dark Mountain and an editorial role on an acupuncture magazine, I have little to show for my efforts. But I am a profoundly different person now. All of the work has been happening beneath the surface: in freeing my body and heart of the false lessons they were taught; in learning to be human; in learning to be.

The demands of writing and Daoism often seem diametrically opposed. The Daoist approach is to quieten the mind, to anchor it in the body, to bring an end to thoughts and speculations – the mental froth and foam so vital for the writer's work. I'm not sure I'm totally done with words yet, though. Part of me still believes that it is possible to use them not merely to generate more words and draw people into another bootless round of intellectuality, but to make new connections, to show things in a different light, to knock loose a piece of the puzzle, to help us remember something we didn't know we'd forgotten.

But, for now, I've said all I have to say.

*

Sit down somewhere quiet. Make yourself comfortable. Now:
Do nothing.

AVA OSBISTON

[above] Pre-flight [p.216] Mother's Face

Yorkshire Dales (Photos: Rebecca Chan)

Ava Osbiston

Gathering

Just along from the compost toilet, nestled in the long grass, is a whole skeleton. Smooth, and cleaned as if with a scrubbing brush, and lying as if the fox had lain down and its flesh had simply disappeared. The teeth come loose as I pick up the skull; later I spend a good hour trying to puzzle which holes they go into. The ribs gather together in my hand, though they had not grown to touch like that. They become my teeth.

Down an alley, behind a mechanics workshop, is a cage filled with undulating blackness. The smell of butyl rubber is compelling. People always want to sniff it once I've made it into some bag or costume. In this state, however, it's a sweaty and grim pile, dribbling unidentified juice as I separate the squeaky tyre carcasses. The mechanic is pleased to be rid of them.

Ullswater is glass smooth in front of the canoe. I'm not good at controlling the paddle nor, therefore, the direction, and we crash up on the beach with a scrunch. The geese that live there have strewn feathers like a map of where they've waddled and where the wind has blown them. The feathers snuggle in the crevice between the windscreen and dashboard as we drive home.

In my bedroom I have five skulls in a row on a shelf. Two foxes, two sheep and a deer. I wanted to wear the fox skeleton I found last year. I wanted to become it, to amalgamate the matter into me. I made earrings from the shoulder blades.

I want to wear the urban detritus too, to show the dissonance inside of me on my outside. I am not (yet) moving back to the land, I am not yet wearing buckskin, just vintage polyester.

I have gathered myself from nature and from the city. Black rubber flesh, feathers, bleached hair, bones, fur, bare skin and grit.

Mike Cipra

Pharaoh Ed

'Let me say, at the risk of seeming ridiculous, that the true revolutionary is guided by great feelings of love.'
– Che Guevara

Picture a pyramid on fire, thousand-year-old redwoods behind it swaying in waves of heat, dazed hippies congregating in front of the hand-plastered monument and black government helicopters hovering around the burning pyramid like moths, all of us caught in the same moment of creation and destruction. Who can say where a story begins, it's as arbitrary as a dog deciding to defecate on a freshly mown lawn. Or a monarch butterfly hungrily entering a flower. How can we understand the miles that insect has come, or the bacteria growing inside a mutt's small intestine? It is simply too much to comprehend all at once, death and life leading to more death and life, and so we are forced to choose a moment and climb through it to understanding.

Ed and I built a pyramid, and our structure grew as our followers grew (as this story does) in alternating bursts of energy and digression. This is the beginning of a manifesto: the hundreds of human beings here on this land (not our slaves, never our slaves) are tired of consuming shrimp or diamonds or shoes or pornography or candy bars or bottled water or whatever adulterated version of the world is for sale. We are prepared to walk away from America, forsaking its steak-and-butter heart, turning away from its lost soul. We have gathered to create something different, to pitch in and sing the old songs around campfires and pray to the diverse goddesses and protest the never-ceasing war that the rich wage against the poor and that progress wages against nature; until what we are building spontaneously combusts, and since it is in flames already, we will climb through the fire together to understanding. Do you have a moment?

Yes, your answer is yes.
Keep this pyramid burning in your mind.

*

Back in the '80s, Ed and I squatted together in Orange County. The girl we were both desperately in love with slept on the ground between us every night. Meet Mona Machuca: a beautiful Mexican punk with a safety pin through her septum and a heart that melts like a globally-warmed glacier when you get close. Mona's the first poet I've ever met – tagging her verses on trains and painting lyrical truths in fat, glowing letters in the steep concrete channels that strangle southern California's rivers.

All three of us were kicked out of our houses around the age of 13, and we found each other the way lost people always seem to. Ed calls this principle The Internal Radar of Desperation. The three of us built a little stick hut in the scrub forest of Laguna Hills and lived off food we could steal.

My go-to dish was beer and hot dogs pinched from the Circle K. We cooked the wieners on eucalyptus branches, which imparted to our processed meat bullets this wonderful, exotic flavour that would get us talking about places in the world where we might one day live, work, and learn to communicate.

Ed preferred vegetables. Raw ones. I remember one time we were strutting along the street in Costa Mesa, la de da, and out of freaking nowhere he shoves my body like a wedge through the door of a Wendy's or some other purveyor of fast food, and I don't even have time to ask, man what the hell are you doing? Ed walks directly to the salad bar, and without hesitating he picks up a tub of ranch dressing, pours it over the greens in the serving bowl, then picks the whole thing up and walks off with it. A young punk with a green Mohawk, stealing corporate veggies in broad daylight.

Ed's salads had a simple and crunchy charm, and my eucalyptus wieners were decent, especially with lots of beer, but neither of these dining experiences approached Mona's speciality. Mona was the best squatter cook of the three of us, mostly because she was also the best thief. When she opened a can of refried beans, avocados magically appeared from her pockets. Ripe avocados! There was a never-ending bottle of hot sauce in camp, courtesy of Mona, with precious red-and-orange habanera blood to burn your lips and tongue and whatever else got in the way. And damn if a package of tortillas didn't materialise out of thin air... and then there was cheese. For hungry punks, cheese is a goddamn sacrament.

Anyway, the three of us would sit around a fire eating what we had gathered from the fat of America and telling stories about the magic we could scrape from our dreams... sort of like the first human beings on this continent. Today, it's hard for me to even look at a can of refried beans and keep my shit together. Here's the terror of memory: when you suffer loss, when you lose someone really important to you, it doesn't just happen once. You get to keep losing that person throughout your life, and small, otherwise insignificant objects – cans of beans, empty beer bottles, a long black hair on an avocado – become the signposts of absence.

*

When Federal Marshall Mike Dunn pulls his cruiser to the front gate of Ed's farm, our pyramid is half-completed. Straw bales are going up as fast as hippies can raise them, which is to say not super-duper fast. There are extended breaks – smoke breaks, meal breaks, child-rearing breaks, guitar and drum circle breaks that stretch time like hot rubber – and then, suddenly, spurts of collective human energy propel our pyramid upward toward the sun. Ed greets Marshall Mike Dunn by slowly extracting a ceramic pipe and plastic lighter from his overalls and handing them to the federal law enforcement officer. I stop slapping down mud plaster and shift the child's weight on my back. I see a great deal of sunlight reflecting off Ed's face. He is either weeping or sweating.

Now sure, this is Humboldt County, and we all have the fine fortune to live in the weed-legal State of California, but if I'm not mistaken, that's a federal cop. In the United States of America, the federal police are under oath to fight a vicious and uncompromising war on drugs, and let's check our facts, this same war on drugs is funded by your tax dollars to the tune of $700 a second. Seven hundred dollars this very second. And this one. And this one... I am watching my friend offer cannabis to a motherfucking federal policeman.

Marshall Mike Dunn sets his hand on Ed's shoulder. The two men walk to the edge of this property, where farm meets forest, the redwoods stretching toward heaven like perfect beings.

We are finished.

I am absolutely sure of it until the federal marshall takes his first hit. I shudder, and the little human being lashed to my back sighs too as she passes water on me. It is pure relief for both of us.

Marshall Mike Dunn stays on. He doesn't quit his job or come live here, but he lends his expertise, becoming our part-time logistics lieutenant. We need him, desperately. Hippies and dropouts and punks are pouring in by the hour. Where are all these people *coming from*? The farm looks like a Grateful Dead concert back when Jerry was alive, freaky folks and pierced mellow souls juggling fire and playing hackey-sack. We need latrines and running water and food and rules, yes, rules for keeping all these human beings alive in the same space.

When Marshall Mike Dunn and I try to make Ed aware of the rather pressing sustainability issues of our growing community, he cuts us off abruptly.

'This is the reality we're creating,' he says like the Pharaoh he is becoming, staring at his growing pyramid in the June fog. 'We are the last remaining bubble in the dirty bathtub of America. Embrace the chaos or get the fuck off my land.'

*

Ed was Mona's boyfriend from the time they were both 11. They lost their virginities to each other very young. Or maybe they presented these virginities, like gifts in small mahogany boxes, with great care and delicacy. Or maybe they had sex like frightened children. Can't say. I wasn't there at the time.

When I arrived, things got sticky. I loved Mona Machuca like... well, I won't say a man, because that's just coarse. Mona and I shared a needle for two years, and that's about as intimate as you want to get with another one of these semi-conscious monkeys that have overrun the planet. Once you have grown into addiction with someone, you know no other need. You have climbed inside her skin, and she has climbed inside yours, and you have both break-danced to an endless song. All I'm trying to say is there's a permanent place hollowed out by that kind of love.

Have you ever felt hollowed out by love?

Yes, your answer is yes.

*

I've been thinking about children a lot these days. Not having them, just, you know, nurturing them. After all, my official revolutionary title is Keeper of the Child. Here's my biggest, broadest concern: what does a child need in order to become something other than a tool? What does a child need to become a questioning life-form? Ed says we invite ourselves to our own destinies, but sometimes I think Ed's full of shit. I believe we just react to the reality into which we're born. Along the way, fate beats our hearts around, like a child striking a *piñata*. Eventually, the bright muscle splits open, and out spills candy, streamers, butterfly wings, words…

Case in point: the squatting days. Christmas. Me, Ed and Mona, opening our hearts around a campfire. Lonely kids reacting to the dysfunctional core of America, our families, and the current of substance abuse that swept through our lives. In my own family's case, the Republican Party was mixed in the steady flow of pills and vodka. The most prized family possession, until I took it off the wall and burned it in a gasoline fire, was a framed photograph of Mom and Dad with the Gipper and Nancy, all of them looking like perfect wax sculptures, Nancy telling me with her half-empty (half-full?) martini glass eyes, Just Say No, Just Say No, Just Say No…

Flash forward. It's the mid-aughts. Twenty years after our punk days. I have become what our society calls a fuck-up: ex-con, environmentalist, worker of odd jobs, unpublished writer, and everything else you can't put on a resumé. Not to mention the fact that I've recently participated in the torching of an urban assault vehicle dealership in the greater Los Angeles area. Picture electric-yellow Humvees going up in flames, carcinogens rising in a nasty pillar of smoke. Are you are starting to see a pattern in my reaction to the reality into which I was born? Is it foreshadowing if I have already revealed that our pyramid burns while government helicopters hover around it?

No, it is not foreshadowing; it's all one long shadow from the same fire.

As those Humvees smouldered, I was considering my limited options. I already knew, from two years working in the kitchen of the Riverside County Correctional Facility after being arrested aged 18 with four ounces of pharmaceutical-grade morphine, that prison is not a swell place. I do not like floors slick with grease, men penned like animals amid the constant threat of sexual violence, and mashed potatoes drawn from boxes.

So, using the complimentary internet access at the Long Beach Public Library, I track down Ed. Goddamn if that vegetable-loving punk hasn't turned into a farmer! Yessir, he's certified organic – purchased a couple of acres of productive land in Humboldt County and started growing his own salads.

Correction: he and Mona Machuca bought a couple of acres together. You see, they're married.

Does this bother you?

I stare at Ed's question on the screen, thousands of books stacked in perfect rows around my solitary organism, and I remember what it was like to live outside with her, our arms sore, our bodies bouncing between heaven and hell, two monkeys hunkering under trees in the rain. Mona reciting her poetry in the rain. And there is the night I don't remember too. She told me afterwards that she was up until sunrise squeezing my face, feet, hands. Punching me, kicking me with her boots, keeping me awake, breaking ribs to save me. I write back into the chill of cyberspace: *No, I am not bothered in the slightest that my friends are in love.*

They let me stay in a beat-up Airstream on the corner of the property. My arrival coincides with a late-summer Humboldt County thunderstorm, so the first week I spend emptying buckets of rain, smoking roll-up cigarettes, and reading the biography of Ernesto 'Che' Guevara – the thousand-page number. Highly recommended.

The second week, Ed asks me to work the farm with him. Mona just can't do it anymore. Her belly looks as if it is about to split apart and drop a watermelon every time she takes a step. They are cultivating organic everything: broccoli and squash and basil and chard and beets and onions. And my favorite, Indian corn. It has to be picked, then shucked in the warm sun. Ed and I sit, pulling back husks to uncover kernels in every shade of red, blue and yellow. Each ear is a revelation, a unique mosaic of genetic history and possibility.

For four days in this florescence of corn, Ed and I rap about our personal stories, the peculiar cross-pollination that generated three punk hippies. I guess I should say three and a half, as Mariposa Karma Shepherd-Machuca is due around the end of September. Mariposa was conceived on a rocky beach just north of Mona's native Guerrero Negro, near as the happy couple can figure. It is pure therapy for me to be around people with this much love. The last time was long ago in the scrub forest of Southern California. Hot dogs on eucalyptus sticks. Now, we are harvesting from the earth instead of from convenience stores. I am happy for my friends. I am happy for another chance, for the child, for the diversity of each ear of corn. Any envy I might once have felt is being shed like a dry husk in the sun.

*

The thing that impresses me most about Che Guevara's life story is that here's this Argentine fellow, more adventurous than thoughtful at 23, jumping on motorcycles and boats and buses, having passionate affairs with women and drinking plenty of cheap, free or stolen wine. On this path of self-discovery – a pretty normal one for a middle-class young man – he begins to feel discomfort. He begins to question. He witnesses the American overthrow of a democratically-elected government in Guatemala, and this he can't let go. The deaths. The suffering, so that American businessmen can have a dictator who invites them to dinner. Ernesto takes one or two small leaps – Mexico, a child – and all of a sudden he's in the Sierra Maestra with Fidel, mounting an armed revolution.

I hadn't known that a revolution can be motivated by anyone… that it doesn't take a saint. Before Che became an icon, he was a person like us, who drank and fell off motorcycles and got his heart beat around as well.

*

Ed and I are coming back along West End Road in *La Chingada Dulce* (Mona's affectionate name for the farm truck she and Ed retooled to run on liquefied French fries and cantaloupe rinds). We're singing Social Distortion's cover of a Johnny Cash classic, raucous loud karaoke with crackling accompaniment from the truck's stereo. *Down, down, down, the flames getting higher*.

We just unloaded hundreds of pounds of organic produce at the North Coast Co-Operative Market... and received a fat cheque for it. The money is enough to get Ed and Mona through the birth of their little girl. Have you ever felt like it's all going to be OK? Like you can just take a breath and finally live?

For me, it feels like the old days, when we'd pair up to steal beer or food or even, one time, a vehicle, a Mercedes with keys glowing like hot coals on the car seat. Of course, this is different, within the law. But it still feels like a score for pulling vegetables from the earth.

'Five thousand dollars!' I yell into the wind.

'Yessir,' Ed grins. 'Folks around here are willing to pay a little extra to eat food that isn't bombarded with chemicals.'

'Remember when we used to eat for nothing? Remember when we stole and searched through dumpsters and told stories around a campfire?'

'That wasn't a sustainable situation.'

'Fuck sustainable. That was the most alive I've ever felt.'

Ed mashes on the brakes, and *La Chingada Dulce* comes to a shivering halt. Ed grabs my shoulder and squeezes like he's trying to pop a balloon.

'Don't say that again.'

'Hey, ease off. What the hell's wrong with you?'

'You just said the moment you are in is not the most vivid of your life. You said "fuck sustainable". If I hear any trash like that coming from your windpipe after my daughter is born, I will personally kick your ass off my property.'

'C'mon, we were just bullshitting.'

'Do you still burn things, Richard?'

Deep breath.

'I don't burn organic vegetables or people that I love, so you don't have to worry. I love living here with you and Mona. Please don't make me leave.'

'Houses, cars, factories, those sorts of things. Do you still burn them?'

'I haven't torched anything since I moved up here.'

'What good does it do?'

'Maybe it's the best way I can think of to fight.'

'Fight what?'

'Come on, man. You know this. All the planet's power and resources are flowing into corporations and getting ground into plastic bags and cans of sprayable cheese and disposable diapers and what the fuck ever. What can you do to stop it, except burn down the corporations?'

'Corporations are insured.'

'Burn down America then. No insurance to cover that.'

'Even if you succeed in burning down America, which is pretty fucking unlikely, they're building this same model just about everywhere in the world.'

'So what do we do, Ed? Give up? Do we hunker down in Humboldt County and try to forget that it's all turning to dogshit?'

'What we have to do,' he says quietly, 'is eliminate the demand for what civilisation is currently producing. And we start with food. We stop buying potatoes dipped in fungicide and tomatoes with fish genes inserted into their DNA and corn so inbred that it has no natural resistance to insect invasions. People need to realise that eating is as intimate as we get with the Earth. At least until we die.'

It gives me goosebumps to hear Ed's voice articulate the issue so clearly, devoid of sentiment, like we're a couple of swordfish laid out on the table about to be filleted. That's the hard punk in him and the human being who is about to become a father and the future Pharaoh, all at once. This moment in *La Chingada Dulce* is the window to understanding our revolution, and you are about to be propelled through it.

West End Road curves east from Arcata and cosies up next to the Mad River before cutting into the valley where Ed's farm sits. The road is small and moves as the river does, the kind of road that locals drive too fast out of familiarity, boredom and sometimes recreation. There are blind corners where redwoods rise and constrict the road to a single lane, and spots where the view opens up onto organic farms and family ranches where horses romp among fresh clover. A hazardous and beautiful ride, especially at sunset, when deer are liable to bolt across the rain-slick road in front of you.

The windows are down. Hurtling through the valley towards us is another vehicle. We cannot see it yet but we can hear it cutting the corners hard, accelerating, tires playing the asphalt.

'That motherfucker,' Ed says, throwing on the brakes and backing into a farmer's driveway.

'What's up?'

'This kid from Blue Lake likes to drive through here like it's the goddamned Formula One. I'm going to get his licence plate and call the sheriff.'

'You're going to report a joyrider to the cops?'

'Fuck yeah I'm reporting him. I think he drives through here drunk.'

'Man, you have *changed*.'

'Did you know Mona likes to take walks on this road?'

'I didn't know that.'

'Look, it's OK to change, Richard. It's OK for us to be different than the story we've always told the world about ourselves.'

There is a long screech, longer and closer than the others. Friction for far too long. Then a wet, sickening thud, and after that, the bright sound of metal crumpling.

A terrible silence follows. I look at Ed. He shoves *La Chingada Dulce* into gear. A hundred yards up the road, a Ford pickup has flipped over. Wheels still spinning. That fresh. A bleeding animal is screaming inside the cab.

Ed cranks on the parking brake and hops out. I'm sitting in the truck like an idiot. Just sitting there, looking at the thing like you might look at a movie screen. And as this horrible movie comes slowly into focus, I see her, the one I lose, over and over, her legs twisted sickeningly.

I don't remember exiting the truck, but now I'm on top of her. I keep pumping on her chest and breathing in her mouth even though I know it is for me. I feel one of her ribs break under the weight of my hands. Ed slaps me and I pull away from her, crying hard. He picks her up and carries her to *La Chingada Dulce*. Puts her in the front seat. Turns the vehicle around, and drives Mona's body back down West End Road, towards Mad River Hospital.

*

You have kept the pyramid burning in your mind. Good work. The authorities are coming in helicopters and gasoline-powered engines to put out the fire and arrest the ringleaders of this inconvenient political and social flare-up. But the ringleaders, and indeed most of us, will vanish into the ancient forest of America. Mariposa is swaddled to my back, and I am well inside the curtain of redwoods. This child, who was cut from her dead mother's body, is now my responsibility. I am Keeper of the Child. Ed will meet us at rendezvous points that have been established throughout the construction phase.

I dream of a time when Mariposa will grow old enough to feel hunger for the verses her mother composed. There are places in the concrete channel of the strangled Los Angeles River that still bear Mona's mark. When Mariposa asks what her mother felt, how brightly she burned in this world, I will take her to see paint and promise, to see her mother's badass poetry. I want the girl to question me too, to ask whether I loved Mona or whether I just loved the needle and the fire and the comfort of her next to me while I tried to die.

I dream of a time when Mariposa will grow old enough to question everything: her father's choices, this path we are walking, the need for her mother's massive pyramid and my need to make it a pyre, the consumption of shrimp or diamonds or shoes or pornography or candy bars or bottled water. This is the moment we are organising for, this moment, right now, the one that causes us to question. In this moment, the pharaohs and the false idols fade away, and all that is left are flawed people who either accept the world they are given or work for a better one.

CAROLINE ROSS

Three hand-hewn knives with blades of flint, bronze and iron

Caroline Ross

Three Blades

I made these knives in the Devon woods during days which spanned epochs – a unique week called 'The Blade', designed to take us through three eras of human technology: the stone, bronze and iron ages.

For the first two days, I sat on a log around a big tarp, holding a rock in my right hand and a flint core between my legs, padded by leather, as I learned from experimental archaeologist Antony Whitlock how to knap the flint to make knives, microliths and hand axes. These would have been used before metal for cutting hides, food and taking down small trees. Day one was spent creating a large mound of artisanal gravel. Miraculously, after waking from a deep sleep, I could create good flakes from my strikes. I pressure flaked the leading edge of one, using an antler tine to form serrations. At the end of the day I set it into a piece of spalted birch with pine pitch and birch tar mixed with charcoal, bound with nettle cordage.

On the third day with prehistoric survival teacher Will Lord we built a bronze furnace from mud, straw, horse dung and horsehair. We smashed malachite with rocks to smelt in a crucible, and once we had obtained copper from the bright green rock, we added tin to make bronze. Hide bellows made the charcoal glow hot enough to form the alloy. With beeswax I made the crescent shape of a ceremonial knife and covered it with clay to form a mould, then poured in the molten bronze to take its place and form a blade. Sharpened and polished, I set this into a small piece of birch and oiled it to bring out the grain.

There was also time to make a sword called the 'Ewart Park Leaf', a replica of one belonging to the Iceni, a British tribe from the time of Queen Boudicca. Such swords were raised against invading Romans, but the professional soldiers of that empire had already marched into the iron age, and their similarly-shaped swords could cut clean through the softer bronze.

In blacksmith Dave Budd's replica Saxon forge the last two days were filled with working huge bellows and bringing a hammer down on the anvil. Hitting steel hard while it was still hot enough to transform proved hard. This was my first week working with stone and metal, my hands used to handling the softer materials of fabrics, paper and paint. There is no place for a tentative touch in the forge. When the blade was good enough, I plunged it into tallow to cool, and later into water to quench it. To temper the blade I heated it in the fire until it showed a specific series of different reds and purples, difficult to discern against the falling light of the fifth day. It lay on a shelf all night cooling and resting, as to haft it now could cause it to shatter.

Finally, I chose a piece of pear wood and shaped it with another knife and rasp for a handle, burning a hole for the tang with a small red-hot rod of iron. Heating the tang, I burned the knife into its housing and set it there with a little glue, then polished the wood and oiled it. Once home I made leather and buckskin for knife sheaths for the two metal blades, and neck cords from which to hang them when in use.

I want to make everything once. When I transform natural materials into what I need, I find myself transformed. When I cut away what is unnecessary, I am also shorn of the inessential. When I take care to finish carefully what is roughly made, some deep part of me is fulfilled. Perhaps it seems simplistic, but it is a method which works: to make metaphors real with practical action, craft and hand work. Then, magically, they are no longer terms of speech, or nice ideas. My sword is real, my knives are sharp, the leather is supple, the cordage holds fast.

Jeri Reilly
Subsist!

A peasant girl stands near me as I write. She stands in a field alone, barefoot. The field looks to be freshly reaped, perhaps only the gleaning left to be done. The sun sets behind her, a skylark hovers above. In the background, a cluster of dwellings – a small village – is moored low to the ground. The girl's face is lifted toward the distance, alert, listening. She holds a sickle in her right hand as if she's just used it, or is about to use it.

Why have I taped a print of this 19th-century painting to the wall above my desk? Why do I feel kinship with this peasant girl? Solidarity? Why do I imagine the curved reaper in her hand could be like my pen? Is it a tool or a weapon? What is she trying to tell me that I need to know now?

Peasant is a word we've been alienated from for a very long time. The land-based subsistence way of life of the peasant was a backward stage of human history, we believe, not yet civilised, a mere prequel, of no relation to our own. The dictionary defines 'peasant' as one who lives in the country and works the land. As surely most of our ancestors once did, and as many people still do in those few places on the Earth not yet penetrated by the market economy. But we're unable to see the peasant in this way. Despite what the dictionary says, peasant is used as a pejorative, as a term of abuse even.

Subsistence is another word we've been alienated from. We believe it means barely surviving, eking out an existence due to a lack of resources or a lack of development. Despite what we've learned in school, at its root, subsistence means existence, independence, stability. It also means to stand still or firm, as in a field one has just helped to reap. The dictionary tells me its origin is the Latin *subsistentia*, which was a borrowing from the Greek *hypostasis*, meaning foundation, substance, reality. When the first Christian missionaries arrived near Bde Maka Ska, a lake in what is now the city of Minneapolis not far from where I live, they were especially appalled by one characteristic of the indigenous Dakota people who lived there – that they did not accumulate, stockpile or store. That they shared. That they were content to have what they needed to survive. That they therefore merely *subsisted.*

There's a story in the picture taped above my desk. I'm trying to read it. The peasant girl in the picture could be 16 or 17, possibly a bit older. Her stance is solid, straight, with a hint of defiance. She holds a tool with which to defend herself and her land, if need be. When I say *her* land, I don't mean that she owns it. As we know, peasants didn't and don't own land. They *inhabit* the land and work the land according to the seasons and customs and traditions of their particular place. In this story, ownership – or private property – is what encroaches from the edges of the picture.

It's what threatens. It's what we know of as the enclosure of the commons. The clearing hoarding mining of the land, the reaving of the common wealth. *Privatisation* is another gloss that's used today, and precisely, since 'private' derives from *privatus,* meaning bereaved, set apart, and then from *privare,* which means *deprive.* Perhaps what the peasant girl listens for are the hoof beats of the landlord's agent bearing the eviction notice. As we today stand listening for the bearing of the extinction notice.

But for now, in the moment of the girl in the field, all is still. It's the golden hush of the gloaming, the only sound the skylark, and high above a silent sickle of moon. No planes, no cars, no ticking clocks.

I want to know her name. We know that she and her people will resist and revolt and stand their barefoot ground. And we know how it will turn out. They will lose their land and their village home, and the song of the skylark. Those who survive the enclosures and clearances and evictions will be shunted to the city, into factories, their bodies, their labour, their land, all become commodities. And here we are today. Just this week, more news that the skylarks in Europe are in dire decline, no longer able to subsist on the commodified lands of the market economy.

I studied European history at university. Why didn't I learn about the peasant uprisings and revolts, the refusals to be severed from the land and shunted into factories? We learned about the revolutions of 1848, but we weren't taught that it was just one year in a long procession of rebellious years, of centuries of peasant, artisan, worker revolts that continued sporadically all the way down, we could possibly say, through 1968, to the Extinction Rebellion breaking out first in London and revelling all the way here to Minnesota.

With the peasant girl beside me, standing on her land, I can see the uprisings and protests were a collective *cri de coeur* of human beings whose habitat was under assault. We say clearances, confiscations, evictions. And surely, to be dispossessed of your home is a trauma, a heart-severance. I now question if we can say that most of the protests and uprisings were political struggles per se. Or were they eruptions of frustrated need and desire to live freely on land they were accustomed and deeply attached to with their hearts and hands?

We weren't taught about this first dispossession. What we were taught was a kind of magical history that framed the 'birth' of capitalism as a kind of virgin birth of a new saviour – the market economy – with the *cultural* achievements that were among its fruits, such as this 19th century painting of a peasant girl and the art museum in which it hangs; and, today, the productions of the Royal Shakespeare Company supported with the help of BP. But even the word 'culture' once meant a tilled piece of land, and its root, 'cult', meant to inhabit or protect with worship or devotion.

The enclosures, if they were taught at all, were taught as agricultural reform. The contemporaneous colonial conquest that fanned out across the globe from European – and then American – capitals was taught, and is still being taught, as 'development'.

*

May 1970. After years of protests against the war in Vietnam, it was revealed that the US government had secretly expanded the war and was bombing Cambodia. Two peasantries were now being burned and asphyxiated with weapons such as napalm – which makes human skin peel off – and their crops and forests defoliated with Agent Orange, which would kill over 400,000 people, maim the health of some four million, and leave behind a lengthening trail of birth defects.

Many students, including some of us at the University of Minnesota, went on strike, and massive nonviolent, sometimes violent, protests erupted. Barricades were thrown up across the main road through campus. Police helicopters hovered to drop tear gas on the students gathered on the quad. Police beat students on their heads and backs with batons. But why were we – of a generation that was safe and secure and well-fed – protesting? Surely many were protesting the draft. But as I remember it, the protests were overwhelmingly a response to moral injury. To the knowledge that our own people, our own government, were inflicting unspeakable violence and horror on another people. On a people who tilled their land and lived in huts clustered together in small villages.

Looking back, I wonder if the killings that year by local government forces of protesting students at Kent State and Jackson State universities were an historic echo of those thousands upon thousands of peasants and workers and townspeople massacred during protests and rebellions against enclosures of the commons, against high rents and taxes, hunger and impoverishment, against the conditions brought on by the market economy. Such as the 3,500 peasants, villagers and townspeople killed in Norfolk during the mass uprising of 1549.

In a curriculum heavy with English history, we were taught nothing about Kett's Rebellion. I would have wanted to know that Robert Kett, the yeoman landowner who led the rebellion by first taking down his own enclosures, petitioned the King with a list of Requests and Demands, such as:

that henceforth no man shall enclose,

that all rivers may be free and common to all men,

that all marshes that are holden by the King's majesty may be free rent,

that it not be lawful to the lords of any manor to purchase lands freely and to let them out again to their great advancement and to the undoing of your poor subjects, and

we pray that all bond-men may be made free, for god made all free with his precious blood shedding.

In a speech from under an oak tree, Kett asked:

Shall they, as they have brought hedges about common pastures, enclose with their intolerable lusts also all the commodities and pleasures of this life, which Nature, the parent of us all, would have common and bringeth forth everyday…?

The answer, of course, is yes they would. The enclosures will continue, without stopping, until the Earth can no longer 'bringeth forth' life. The follow-up question I now want to ask is: how long after the land was enclosed did it take to enclose our minds? So that even today, reading about the Kett rebellion, some might think it radical, unreasonable, and certainly impractical. Some might also wonder, given that the rebellion failed so disastrously, if Robert Kett should have given up rather than suffer the torture and execution that awaited him – to be hung in chains over the high wall of Norwich Castle, and left to die slowly of starvation.

But, for now, looking at the painting, I'm able to glimpse a time before our minds were enclosed, when a peasant was *a country person who worked the land*, when a people would fight against their severance from the land and from their means of survival. A time when they still knew where their means of survival lay.

When classes resumed after the student strike, I was startled to hear a history professor say that the counter-culture rebellion was 'the last gasp of the pre-industrial age'. I couldn't make out if he considered that a good or bad thing. We'd been taught that all of life's current benefits and comforts were the result of the Industrial Revolution. And that all before was famine, misery and toil; plague, ignorance and filth. Most people I know who went to university still believe this. At some level, people today are still congratulating themselves for not being peasants, despite that their cars and chemicals and tumble dryers are annihilating life on Earth.

The counter-culturists and anti-war protesters of the time were often described as dirty. *Dirt. Dirty. Soiled.* Yes, I see that even the dirt, the soil under our feet – the 'sponsor of life' as Wes Jackson calls it – is a pejorative, a term of abuse even.

The hippies and students in the neighbourhood where I lived were known as back-to-the-landers in the city. We were growing and cooking and sharing our food, in resistance to the factory food and ready meals that were then enclosing farm-grown, home-cooked food. In our house, we ground wheat berries and corn with a hand mill, we cooked on a solid-fuel range, grew our produce out back. We relearned how to can our produce, bake our bread, publish our newsletters, make our music.

Although most of us had grown up in the suburbs, we seemed to be reverting to values no longer operating in the expanding consumer regime. We started food cooperatives, supplied in large part by local farmers. These carried most things in bulk, and you had to bring your own containers. They were managed mostly by volunteers. When I look back now, I'm surprised that we did these things so naturally.

Ours was an old immigrant neighbourhood of small workers' houses in Minneapolis, built before indoor plumbing and electricity. The houses themselves offered a history lesson with their stone cisterns under the kitchen to harbour rainwater, root cellars to keep the produce, fruit and nut trees, a lack of central heating. When the government slated our houses and gardens for demolition as part of a redevelopment project – what they called 'urban renewal' – we stood our ground and fought back for years. This kind of resistance was taking place across the city, and some of the old neighbourhoods were saved.

I always suspected, or hoped, that the professor believed that what the counter-culture harked back to was a good thing. That the counter-culture was a revival, however brief and faint, of some dormant human vitality, of a cellular memory of human life when it was rooted in land, like the way a wild flower will push up through the asphalt of a new road and bloom in defiance like a fist.

*

The young peasant girl. Her face alert, listening. Her way of life on the brink, as life has been ever since the enclosures that were bearing down on her. You can't *inhabit* a place that's under development, where the land under your feet is being auctioned off, the value of it rising and falling based on some distant financial market.

In the dim background of the painting, I see a hayrick. Perhaps it was made that day. People who carry the memory of building a hayrick will tell you it was the toughest job of the harvest. In County Sligo, Ireland, where these ricks were made within living memory, it was said that the making of one hayrick strong enough to withstand the winter rains and wind off the Atlantic required a team of six to eight men working a full day. Their harvest stories are hearty ones, telling of the skills, the wits, the turns of weather, the sharing of the work, and the jokes and stories and songs that accompanied the work.

My mother once told me an unexpected story about a haystack, as they're called in Minnesota. It happened when she was a child of nine, in the midst of the Great Depression. Her father had found work going from town to town, repairing typewriters and adding machines. Sometimes his wife, my grandmother Nellie, went with him. On one of their trips, they brought my mother, who was home from school that day with a cold. It was early spring. The town they drove to, called Belle Plaine, was one of those settler towns, not many blocks long, a town that served the local farm families. Before my grandfather went into the office, where he said he'd be for the rest of the afternoon, he gave Nellie some coins, 'for tea and a bite to eat'.

My mother remembered how cold the wind was that day, how it pierced their spring coats as they walked through the town. Some of the places they saw had steamed up windows and looked like they'd be warm inside. Maybe it was because Nellie was frugal, being that it was the Depression, or maybe there was some other reason they didn't go in any of those places with the steamed-up windows. After they'd walked up and down the main street a couple of times, Nellie said, 'No library'. Even though the sun was getting higher in the sky, they were not getting warmer. Nellie took her scarf off and wrapped it around her daughter's neck and then took her hand and said she'd find them a place to warm up. But she started walking *out* of the town!

Soon they were beyond the sidewalks, walking on a straight gravel road. Finally, Nellie said, 'here we are'. My mother looked around. There wasn't a house or a barn or anything. Just a field and a haystack. But that, my mother said, was it. They climbed to the top of it, and her mother made a little nest for them. They cuddled together there, out of the wind, under the sun. The sky was that crisp spring blue, my mother remembered. She said they fell asleep like that and didn't wake up till the sun wasn't at the top of the sky anymore. That afternoon in the haystack, she said, was the happiest memory she had of her mother.

How did my town-dwelling grandmother know you could build a nest in a haystack? Was it a folk memory? Is it some kind of folk impulse that would take you away from the town and toward the past of the countryside? The old way? I don't know. But I see that the word 'folk' has now stepped onto my page, in its *sabots*, perhaps, or barefoot.

Folk is another enclosed word, not quite a pejorative, but surely a word that denotes a backward stage of human culture, a vernacular stage, when people made their own houses, cradles, coffins; clothing, light, and music. Folk culture, we say, and we think rural, rustic, naïve. But we were all folk before we became consumers, weren't we? If we strip away our modern myth about progress, wouldn't we find naked folk shivering underneath? Wouldn't we find ourselves needing – first and foremost – food, water, shelter? Beneath it all, aren't we creatures of the Earth rather than masters of the universe set to head off to Mars as soon as our ransacking of Earth is completed?

Our world is round but we've been trying for the past several centuries to make it a straight line, a linear zoompath to the future, to the golden city on the hill. Some of us have now left the path that would take us to that city on the hill. We've turned back to the dark mountain, where we're not alone and apart anymore. Where we stand in solidarity.

Looking out from the mountain, I see now that we have no future. The future is a fable, if not a lie. What we do possess most dearly is the cycle of the seasons. All life revolves – the day, the year, the sun and moon, our own Earth – the name we've given our home. Our round revolving 'Earth', the same word we use for the soil, the dirt under our feet, the dirt where our old stories can re-root, stories that are seeded and nourished with love.

I wonder now about the far-off gaze of the peasant girl. Did she glimpse the dark mountain in the distance? Is she here with us now, her reaper with the curved blade like a crescent moon, standing with us on the Earth, in solidarity, as we pull down the fences that have kept us apart from our own deep nature, and the nature of the living world?

Rachel Economy

A Home for the Seeds

It was as the floods were coming in and the steam burning through the windows that we gripped our spades in our teeth and climbed into the mouth of the mountain to build secret homes for the seeds.

We did not know each other, or we thought we did not.

We had not been born in the same places. We had never spoken words the others recognised. In the flood, trying to get out of the city, we had found ourselves in a tangle of unmatched tongues and car tires spinning wretched against the finally wet, so wet, too wet soil. Cacophony. An unwieldy din.

But there was a language we held common, a thing that drove us madly into the hills soaking and coughing, our pockets full of sunflowers and fava beans. Call it the language of fertility. The rhetoric of rot. Of reimagining. Call it insanity. Call it a failure to bite down and trudge the proper path and save the proper thing. Call it disease or dis-ease or dissonance or dismantling, all.

Whatever name, we had it. We were, first and foremost, the ones who got out, some privilege and a dash of chance. And we were also the ones who knew that the story of what-to-do-in-case-of-disaster was a made thing, a stitched thing, an invisible law book, something written by five-fingered-hands in one very specific language for one very specific purpose. That the disaster itself was a story too, a real thing, yes, and a real thing that had been made, a written thing. And we were the ones who knew story could, just as truly, be torn up, dug up, restitched, by hands, by briars, by sharks' teeth snagging. We were the imaginers. The anxious creators, for whom no law was obvious and no story a static end. We had no set idea of how precisely to respond to a flood. We were not wed to any particular conversation with G_d about the monogamous needs of animals on large boats that wait out storms. Neither were we looking to save the microwaves.

And we were the ones who had no children. Or whose children had already gone. To the waters, to the white and hungry guns, to the longing. We were the ones who had no seeds.

So we found some. In the backs of our closets, in the corner stores standing ankle-deep in water, in the jars on the tilting kitchen shelves. And we gripped our spades in our teeth, and we looked sideways as the streets began to buckle and fold into foothills, and we saw each other limping, and rolling, and running, pockets spilling over with hard-shelled children, with descendants of future trees, and we reached out as we ran, and we gripped each other's hands in our hands.

It was the queerest thing, like a bird in love with a sturgeon, a family of defectors, arms empty of objects and pockets emptied into soil above the water line, saving no wealth or infrastructure, saving the wrong things. A re-kindling, a re-kinning, a reckoning.

All this dying, it has been beyond swallowing.

All those bodies, they came home to the soil. And so we gave them children. Hard-shelled and root-bound. It was a kind of making love to the dead. We slipped seeds into their pockets. Their bodies fertile, already almost soil, meeting the beans, the walnuts, the pits we plunged into the wet ground. The rhetoric of rot. The true nature of kinship: all things becoming other things. Hidden in the mountain, learning each others' languages, guarding, gardening, waiting for the first roots, those parts of the plants called 'radical', to unfurl their faces into the soil.

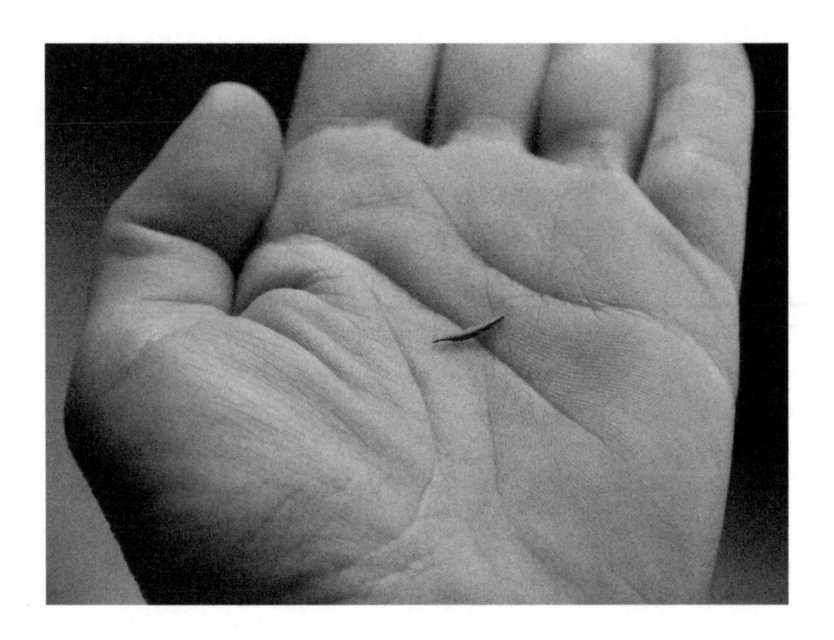

MONIQUE BESTEN
1 Daydream Seed
(*Cosmos bipinnatus* 'Daydream'), *photograph*

[overleaf]
3652 Daydream Seeds
(*Cosmos bipinnatus* Daydream'), *photograph*
One for every day. Ten years of words, ten years of seeds

Seeds are promises always, and beautiful by themselves. But they need to be planted. And even when they are planted, you don't know if the dream of tasty vegetables, juicy fruits or beautiful flowers will come true. Ideas can be seeds, dreams can be seeds, many things can be seeds. Words are seeds. *Cosmos bipinnatus* 'Daydream' thrives in difficult conditions. It grows big and gives lots of flowers. When flowering, the flower can become too heavy for the plant but when grown in groups they support each other. An invitation to the readers of these words: included in this journal are some of the seeds you see on this image. It would be wonderful if you could plant them.

Dougald Hine

The Vital Compass

A conversation with Vanessa Andreotti

The second time I meet Vanessa Andreotti, we're in the lobby of a Paris hotel. There are signs warning guests against trying to get around by taxi. It's Saturday, 1st December, 2018 – or Act III, according to the calendar of the *gilets jaunes* protesters who are converging on the capital for the third weekend in a row, bringing half the city to a halt.

We're here for the Plurality University, a gathering of designers and thinkers and sci-fi writers brought together 'to broaden the scope of thinkable futures'. There are distant sirens and smoke rising from the city below, and it feels like the future already arrived while we were busy looking the other way. So Vanessa and I slip away through the back streets, talking about what happens when the future fails. She's just been back to Brazil, her home country, and she traces the lines that run from an eruption of anger that spilled out onto the streets there five years earlier to the election of Jair Bolsonaro. How much of today's politics, around the world, is shaped by the dawning recognition that the ship of modernity – sailing under the flags of development and progress – is going down?

'A lot depends,' she says, 'on whether people feel that the promises were broken, or whether they see that these were false promises all along.'

The first step is an admission that something has gone badly wrong. This is the advantage that Trump had over Clinton, or the Brexiteers over the Remainers: whatever pile of lies they served it up with, they were able to admit that the ship is in trouble, while their opponents went on insisting that we were sailing towards the promised destination. In Brazil, the promise was that everyone could have the lifestyle of a new global middle class – and when this future failed to materialise, Bolsonaro was able to ride the anger of voters by claiming that it could have been theirs, if it hadn't been for the corruption of his opponents. If the promises were broken, then we look for who to blame and how to take revenge. A lot depends, then, on the recognition that the promises could never have been kept; that they were not only unrealistic, but harmful. For only with this recognition is there a chance of working out what remains, what might be done, starting from the wreckage in which we find ourselves.

For more than ten years, I have been seeking out conversations about what remains, looking for people with whom to think about the wrecked promises of modernity, ways of naming our situation and making it possible to talk together about it. The most illuminating of these encounters have been with people whose thinking was formed by finding themselves and their communities on the hard end of the processes of modernisation. As Gustavo Esteva and I discussed in *Dark Mountain: Issue 4*, there is a sense that the West is belatedly coming to know the shadows of development and progress, shadows all-too-familiar to those unto whom development was done.

Vanessa Andreotti's work deals with these shadows. Her institutional position at the University of British Columbia overlaps with her work as part of Gesturing Towards Decolonial Futures, a collaboration between academics, artists and indigenous scholars and communities. Six months on from that day in Paris, we record a conversation, and as I listen back to the recording, I'm struck by the sense that she is always speaking out of a collective, collaborative, ongoing process of thinking together. Every time we talk, there are new versions of the 'social cartographies', poetic maps that make it possible to have difficult conversations. The maps that emerge from Vanessa's collaborations are boundary objects, places where we meet, where there is a chance of sitting with our discomfort, with our limits, maybe beginning to find a place within a world that is larger and stranger than that allowed for in the ways of seeing that shaped the modern world.

DH Looking back at the Dark Mountain Manifesto, there's a passage towards the end where we talk about 'redrawing the maps', a theme I've found myself returning to regularly over the past decade. The drawing of maps is full of colonial echoes, so we talk about seeking the kind of maps that are 'sketched in the dust with a stick, washed away by the next rain'. It's this image of maps that are explicitly provisional and not pretending to the objective, detached, view-from-above quality that mapping often implies.

That makes me think of what you call a 'social cartography' and the collection of maps that you've built up with your collaborators. Maybe a good place to start is to ask just what this way of mapping means to you?

VA You mentioned the colonial approaches to knowledge production, and I think we started there, with an intention to interrupt this totalising relationship with knowledge. In the work of the collective, we felt that maps – as images that could *visibilise* or *invisibilise* certain things – had the potential not to represent reality but to create metaphors. We wanted to create spaces for difficult conversations where relationships didn't fall apart – and the cartographies have been our main tool for working through the difficulties, the hotspots, the tensions, the paradoxes and the contradictions of these conversations.

So, for example, we have the cartography of 'the house modernity built' which is talking about the fundamental structure of modernity. There are two carrying walls and there is a roof that is structurally damaged, which is why the house is unstable, facing imminent collapse.

We talk about the foundation of the house being the assumption of separability between humans and what we call 'nature'. That separation then generates other types of separation, creating hierarchies between humans, and between humans and other species, and this is our understanding of the foundation of colonialism. In the collective, we don't see colonialism as just the occupation of lands or the subjugation of people; we believe it starts with this foundational separability that interrupts the sense of entanglement of everything, that interrupts the sense that we are part of a metabolism that is the planet and that we belong to a much wider temporality within this metabolism. This separation takes away the intrinsic value of life within a wider whole and creates a situation where we are forced to participate in specific economies within modernity in order to produce value to 'prove' that we deserve to be alive.

In the image of the house, one of the carrying walls is the carrying wall of the Enlightenment, or what we refer to as universal reason – this idea of a totalising, universalising form of rationality that wants to reduce *being* to *knowing*, that then creates a single story of progress, development and human evolution. The other carrying wall is the carrying wall of the nation state, which is often presented as a benevolent institution, but was primarily created to protect capital.

The current roof of the house is the roof of financial shareholder capitalism, which is different from industrial capitalism. We talk about the differences between the two in terms of the possibility of tracing investments and of using the state as a means of both redistribution and some form of checks on capital.

DH The way the state used to act as a stabilising force within the system?

VA Yes, so now we have a speculative financial system where those checks and balances are eroded and where investment is at the expense of others. This investment in destruction is so normalised that even people fighting against climate change or for social justice end up not realising that by using a credit card – or by thinking about the continuity of, for example, our own pensions – we are participating in an economy that is primarily grounded on anonymity and destruction. So there is no way anybody participating in this economy can be innocent, whereas with industrial capitalism, it was much easier to trace the responsibilities: Ford as a manufacturer was embodied in Henry Ford, a person, where it was possible to say, 'You have responsibilities in relation to society, in relation to your employees'. Today, Ford is a shareholder company and I don't know if my pension contributions are already invested there, giving me a shareholder interest.

I'm trying to make it simple enough, without losing the complexity of the connections between these things – because I think what these cartographies do is to connect dots in a way that works against our unconscious desires to not talk about the ways we are complicit in harm.

DH You said that a map like this is not claiming to represent reality, it's offering a metaphor – and that reminded me of a thought about language that I found really helpful in one of your texts. It's a distinction between two ways of understanding what's happening when we use language: one assumes that we are making an objective description of the world; the other sees language as always an action within the world, rather than a description from above.

VA In this sense language *mobilises* realities. So instead of trying to index reality and meaning with a view to this totalising knowledge that can control reality and engineer something, what we do is see language as an entity that plays with us and we play with it. So the relationship with language becomes very different – and that's why also, with the maps, they move and they do what they need to do and they need to change, because they are affectable by the world and by how people interact with them.

We see that some of the maps are more stable than others because they are useful for more contexts, up to a point, but they can't become canonical answers to universal problems. The keeping of the artificiality is really important, I think, because then it draws the attention to the process. It makes it an ongoing movement rather than an accurate description.

DH So going back to the cartography of the house – and the impossibility of not being tangled up with the systems that are perpetrating the destruction – that's clearly part of what you're trying to render visible, which makes for more difficult conversations than the ones that people often want to have. I feel like one of the reasons people shy away from those conversations is because they don't know what to do if they let all this stuff in. It's like a pit of despair opening before them – and so it's easier to go off and have a conversation over here, where we've got some simplified version of the future and of how the world is, that allows us to talk as if we had a chance of setting things right.

Letting go of that is both vertiginously frightening for people – it's like looking off a cliff – and it's also highly moralised. The terrible thing that Paul and I were accused of in the early days of Dark Mountain was 'giving up', and that's about giving up on the stories of progress, giving up the teleological sense of direction and the possibility of mastery. So I'm interested in your experiences of what happens as we create and hold spaces of conversation beyond reform, beyond revolution, beyond any kind of promise of the direction of history.

VA I think the giving up of illusions and seeing disillusionment as a generative thing, this is what we've been looking at. As you said, modernity is falling and we need to create spaces for things to fall apart generatively. Partly these are the connections that need to be made through the cartographies. Partly it's about supporting people to work through denial. In this sense, we have been talking about three denials.

The first is the denial of violence: this house, this system that rewards us and gives us enjoyment and security, was created through violence and it is maintained by violence. So there's an illusion of innocence and a denial of systemic violence that needs to go. Then there's an illusion about linear progress and the possibility of continuity, this is the denial of the limits of the planet. The third denial is the denial of entanglement. We are not separated from the metabolism that is the planet, but there's an illusion of separation – from land, from other beings, from each other, and even within ourselves, from the complexities of our own being. Once you start connecting these three illusions together, there is a falling apart. There's also a sense that if you can't do anything that *leads to* something in a teleological way, you're not doing anything.

This structure of modernity has created a feedback loop that starts with fears: a fear of chaos, a fear of loss, a fear of death, a fear of pain, a fear of pointlessness, worthlessness and meaninglessness that then become allocated desires for specific things. So for example, the fear of scarcity becomes a desire for accumulation. And then these desires, within the modern structures and feedback loops, become entitlements: the desire for accumulation becomes, in turn, a perceived entitlement to property or ownership.

There are several of these feedback loops that make it very difficult for us to imagine anything otherwise or feel secure in embarking on things that could emerge, but that are unfamiliar and that don't feed the feedback loops. At this point, we talk about the grammar of modernity, what makes things legible within modernity. Because of the reduction of being to knowing, legibility and the idea that reality can be indexed is what provides security. So from there we ask: what is the grammar that makes things legible and thus the only things that become real and ideal? If you want to put the world in a box, what is the size of this box and is it a square box? How does the world need to be, in order to be contained in this box? So we talk about *illegibilities*: things that are viable, but unimaginable, unthinkable within this grammar.

DH Possibilities that can't be seen through these lenses.

VA Yes – and because we're working with indigenous knowledge systems, or systems of being, we talk about the problems of trying to graft these systems into the same boxes we are used to. In that sense, we talk about what's *invisibilised*. And there's a need for not trying to make this visible. You need to make what's invisible *visibly absent* first; otherwise, what you're doing is just a translation into the grammar that you already have.

We talk about exiled capacities, which are neurobiological states that may offer different kinds of security or stability, even without having a formalised notion of security. These could help us be together without the need to mediate our relationships in articulated knowledge. Through modernity, we relate to each other through knowledge filters, which makes sense to its grammar – but there are other possibilities for relationship, where these knowledge filters are not as important or as thick as we have been socialised into wanting.

If we are not well in our relationship first with *where* we are – not just in geographical terms, but in a broader sense – there's no chance we're going to be able to have healthy one-on-one relationships. We need to be *there* and then through the unknowability – because *there* is not a knowing place, it's a being place – through the unknowability of this being there is where you can connect with other people. So first, you relate through a vital compass, a compass of vitality. Then you have a more intellectual compass that works with it, but is not more important.

DH That image of a compass of vitality, it makes me think of Ivan Illich talking about conviviality and placing that emphasis on certain ways of being together, coming alive together.

VA That's definitely part of it, but this vitality is not just human. It's through the perception of vitality in everything, the unknowable vitality, that we sense our entanglement with the world.

Suely Rolnik also talks about the vital compass, about how we are being fertilised by the world in unmediated ways, all the time; some gestations come to term, others do not. She talks about the fact that our vital compass is not being given space or developed, so we are having a lot of abortions of possibilities. This is because we want the moral compass to be the only mediator of reality, and this compass is broken.

DH Wow, what a powerful set of images.

VA I know! The abortion of possibilities really struck me... I suppose it's true because if you are afraid of engaging with the world in an unmediated way, you're not going to allow most gestations to come to term. You want to have autonomy and control over the life that you perceive to be only yours.

DH There's a conversation I've had with various people about steering by a sense of what you come alive to – and learning to trust, to pay attention to this subtle sense of vitality. If something is dying a little, notice that, and don't allow anything to be so important that it overrides that awareness and the message it is bringing, the message that something is wrong. To me, this image of the vital compass speaks to that set of conversations and experiences.

VA Suely Rolnik also has ten propositions to decolonise the unconscious. We have translated them from Portuguese in one of the collective's publications. There are five in our version – and I think this little death you are talking about is there in those propositions.

DH That mention of the unconscious brings me to something else I wanted to ask you about. I've noticed you talk about your work as a collective in terms of a form of 'non-Western psychoanalysis'. That struck me as a very curious phrase and I'm interested to hear more about that as a framing of what you're up to.

VA Western psychoanalysis draws attention to the unconscious, to the desires and yearnings that drive our decisions and the ways we think. However, the ontology behind it is either anthropocentric or anthropomorphic. It's all about bodies or archetypes. It's useful, but it doesn't really offer any way to manifest entanglement.

The idea, for example, that the land dreams through us is not contemplated by Western psychoanalysis – but it is contemplated by other cultures, including indigenous cultures that use psychotropics, for example, where an encounter with a being in a plant will give you dreams that you wouldn't have otherwise. These dreams help you work through practical knowledge, knowledge of the psyche and knowledge of the divine, and there are neurological, neurobiological and neurochemical changes too. That is how it becomes neurofunctional.

If these practices are part of your lived reality, you're talking not just about a chemistry of the brain or its biology, but its functionality: how you start to rely on these dreams, not as a different reality for an escape, but as an extension of the same reality. So we're coming from learning about practices that do not see the body as the end, the human body – or even the human mythical frame – as the basis of existence…

DH As the place where the thing that psychoanalytic tradition is dealing with comes to an end, the limit of the reality it can speak of. I see that.

VA Let's take the land as a living entity – not as a concept, but as a manifestation, because there's a difference. A manifestation that is more

Five propositions to decolonise the unconscious

(Creative adaptation by Vanessa Andreotti and Dani d'Emilia, from a text by Suely Rolnik)

1. Activate the vital compass: re-activate the body as a knowing entity that receives and experiences the world as continuous with itself in its living condition, and that is affected by the forces of the world in an unmediated way.
2. Remove the blockages to the difficult experience of making what is strange seem familiar and making what is familiar seem strange in order to register world-interpolations that are always already happening anyway.
3. Do not interpret the resulting vulnerability and its discomfort as a bad thing and do not project fantastic interpretations onto this state of instability. These interpretations usually come from premature responses of a threatened ego, provoked by its helplessness, failures and fears of demotion, rejection, social exclusion and humiliation.
4. Allow what is agonising within you to die without trying to rescue the old state and its sensation of coherence and stability – remember that the vital force needs this space that is being cleared by the death of the old in order to emerge. Stay in this state of uncomfortable instability until the creative imagination can articulate the contours of the new entity that is gestating as a result of the registered encounter with the world. Do not impose limits on the time that the creative imagination needs to support the gestation of the new entity. Do not turn the creative imagination into 'creativity' ready for consumption and reproduction of the status quo.
5. Hold on to the life-affirming yearning that keeps life open to being 'fertilised' by the world and its difference and endless differentiation. Do not negotiate with what obstructs the possibility of life regenerating itself. Calibrate thinking towards its best behaviour: to reimagine its image of the world every time that life demands it to do so.

powerful than just human cognition, but where humans are also part of this manifestation. If we flip that, what possibilities for being and knowing and doing and yearning are opened up? We talk about a metabolic intelligence, we're thinking about a metabolism not only of the Earth but also of what the Earth is embedded in. In this sense, the land is not a resource or an anthropomorphic extension of ourselves, but we are an extension of the land itself.

If you turn everything to an organic metaphor, we can talk about a metabolism that we're part of, a metabolism that is sick or that has a big constipation – a lot of shit for us to deal with! Personal shit, collective shit, historical shit, systemic shit. It needs to pass, it needs to be composted, we need to be attentive to it. This shit involves the systemic violence, the complexities of different forms of oppression, the unsustainability of what gives us enjoyment and security, and the illusion of separation. So the denials are probably the cause of the constipation.

We also talk about a 'bio-internet' and accessing a new operating system with new 'apps' or un-numbing and re-activating capacities that the house has exiled. In that sense, the engagement with indigenous practices is not about coding these practices as an alternative to modernity or as a supplement to modernity. Rather, it relates to (re)learning or (re)creating habits that can help us to figure out if we can interrupt the feedback loops (of fears, desires and perceived entitlements) of the house of modernity in order to open up possibilities that are currently unintelligible and unimaginable.

DH That thought about the possibility of new possibilities brings me back to a phrase of yours that has stuck with me. You talk about 'hospicing modernity and assisting with the birth of something new, undefined and potentially, but not necessarily, wiser'. After we first met, I was teaching on the first course at a school called HOME, and those words of yours became a touchstone for that week. Afterwards, a guy who was there wrote an article for *VICE* and hung his whole piece on those words – except that, firstly, he managed to write you out of the story and just ascribe the words to me, and then he left out the second half, the part about the birth of something new.

What I find striking is that this language of 'hospicing' gets used quite a lot in some of the places and conversations that cross paths with Dark Mountain. However, the other half, the assisting with the birth of some-

THE HOUSE
MODERNITY BUILT

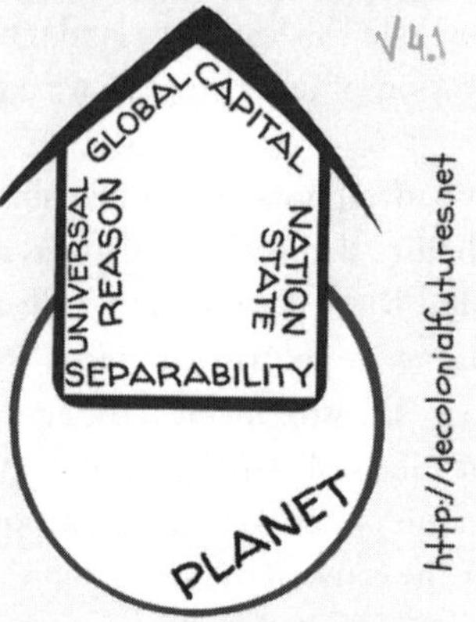

house exceeds limits of planet

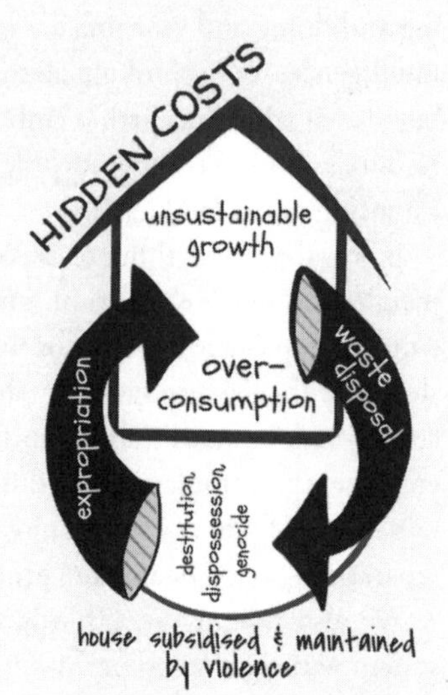

REASONING

dialectical utility maximizing
logocentric evolutionary
Cartesian teleological
allochronic anthropocentric

I think, therefore I am!
I say, therefore it is!
I own, therefore I rule!
I lead, therefore you follow!
I arbitrate, therefore you comply!
I rock, therefore you suck!

(erotic, aesthetic, intuitive, ludic, divine, hilarious, other-than-human)
being reduced to knowing "sausagization"

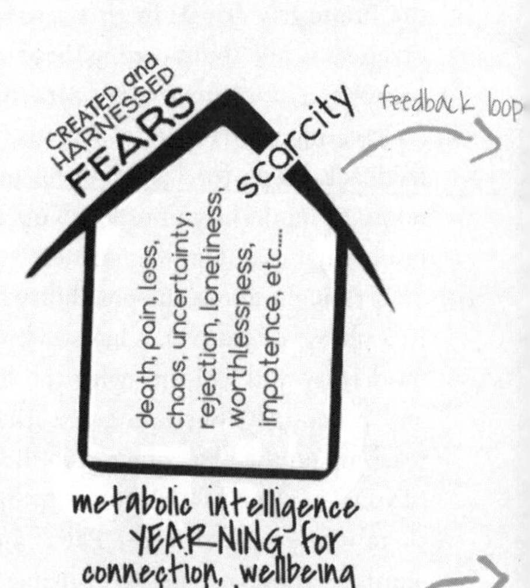

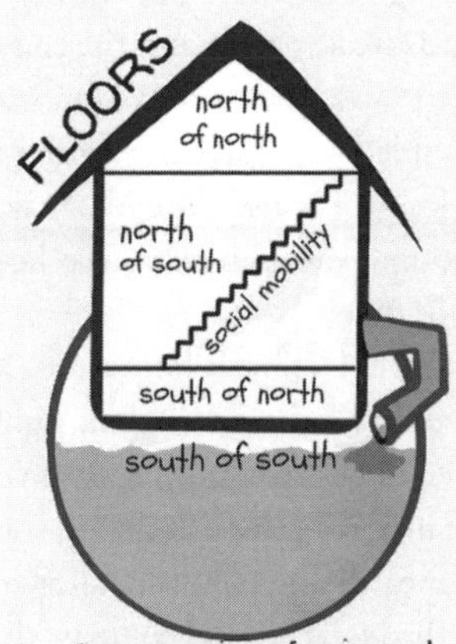

false promise of universal middle class

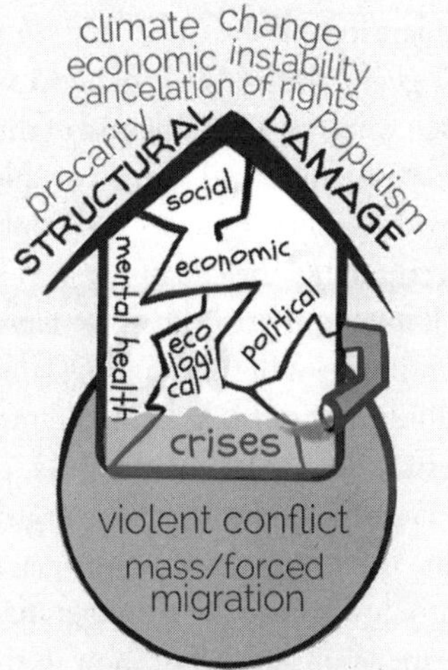

fix? expand? build another? live without? find more planets?

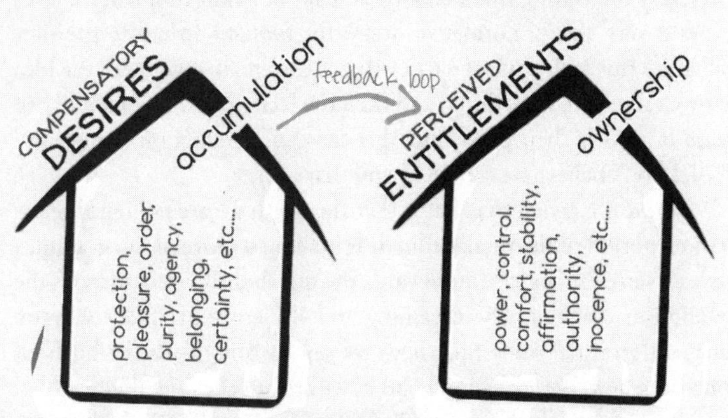

experienced within the house as a felt need for securities and enjoyments tied to the consumption of products, relationships, sensations, narratives, experiences, hopes and fantasies

thing new, is often missing in those conversations. Part of that comes, I suspect, from an inability to see much space in between the end of modernity and the end of *everything*.

I guess that's what Paul and I were trying to name in the *Manifesto*, when we wrote that 'The end of the world as we know it is not the end of the world, full stop.' Then, a couple of years later, in a conversation with David Abram for our second book, I stumbled on a further iteration of that thought: 'the end of the world as we know it is also the end of a way of knowing the world.' That feels to me like somewhere you've been spending a lot of time, finding language for that.

VA I think it goes back to the grammar and the feedback loops, too. So there is this desire for certainty, predictability and totalisation, right? You need to know where you're going, even if it's extinction! It gives you some security. So how do we open up and interrupt these desires in ways that allow us to take an integrative step into the metabolism, allowing the metabolism itself to show us the way through the vital compass that then recalibrates our intellectual compass.

It's very interesting that everywhere I speak about hospicing, there's always a very strong normative desire for *humans* to create the new reality. It's this archetype of agency that is extremely ingrained: the idea that we can create something, and then the lack of faith in humanity to create it, which then plays into this sense of resignation. People say 'Well, I don't believe we can do it', and that's it.

What we are trying to get at is that the death we are talking about is an interruption of the totalisation. If it is about a move of integration, a move towards entanglement, towards the metabolism itself, then it's the metabolism that does the dreaming and the creation. That's why we don't say 'creating' something new, we say 'assisting with the birth' of something new. We are assistants to it, we are not the ones doing it.

DH So it's a humbler role that we might be arriving into, if we're lucky?

VA Absolutely. And it's very different from this bravado thing about saving the Earth or saving humanity or even saving ourselves or our families, prepping for the end of the world. Existentially, it's a very different starting point. It's not even about letting go of the ego, it's shifting existential direction rather than focusing on form: that's why we don't use the word 'transformation'.

We are interested in the shift of direction from the neurobiological wiring of separability that has sustained the house of modernity to the neurofunctional manifestation of a form of responsibility 'before will', towards integrative entanglement with everything: 'the good, the bad and the ugly'. This form of responsibility is driven by the vital compass. It is not an intellectual choice nor is it dependent on convenience, conviction, virtue posturing, martyrdom or sacrifice. You can see this responsibility at work in practices of indigenous and Afro-descendent communities that collaborate with the collective.[1] We have been working on the question of how to invite the interruption of the three denials and the composting of our collective and individual 'shit' in non-coercive, experiential ways.[2]

Notes

1. See bit.do/billcalhoun and bit.do/webofcures
2. See bit.do/decolonialfuturesimpact

Ben Weaver

The Return of Fire

It reminds me of whitewater
from within an eddy
stuffed up a river's sleeve –
both hands full of styrofoam and roses
embracing the paradoxes,
years of shell compressed
at the bottom of this mad time.

I dreamt it while sleeping
in a tangle of cottonwood root
on an eroded bank
near the confluence of universes –
I thought the enemies were far away
cold in the subway or
stuck behind desks and steering wheels.

When I woke it was written
out on wasp paper with beet juice,
the enemy is not a person
the enemy is blindness,
and lack of imagination.

One day there will be forests on Greenland
the land will have risen back up
fires will speckle the darkness
and songs will return again,
refuges will be replenished
the blues having transformed the distances
back to running water,

the sun coming up over a hill
similar to a goddess moving like a grizzly bear,
a dagger laced into her boot.

Nick Hunt

Leaving the Fold

It is dawn in the city of concentric rings. A woman is leaving the Fold and she will not come back. She waits at the gate, which will open soon to reveal the outer zone beyond. On the far side of the wall is greenness, mist and birdsong.

She carries nothing apart from the bag on her back and the suitcase in her hand. The restrictions are strictly enforced; they will confiscate any plastic. Batteries and wearable tech are outlawed too, even rechargeables. There is not much she can take. Not much she will miss.

A crowd of other émigrés waits patiently and quietly, some in small groups but most of them alone. They watch the flaming sky and the sunlight spreading across the wall, illuminating fissures where delving roots have grown. Some stand with their eyes half-closed, as if they might still be asleep. She wonders whether she will encounter them again on the far side of the wall. Whether they will be important to her. Whether anyone will be.

'Are you sure?' he asks once again. He stands tragic in his uselessness, hovering uncertainly, and her heart almost breaks for everything that they shared. She doesn't answer, but takes his hand – a farming tool, blunt and strong, the creases of it scored with grime – and looks back across the Fold, at what she is leaving. The green-roofed domiciles with their squared untidy fields, their orchards and their rows of corn, their allotments, poultry, pigs, polytunnels and pastures. It was all she wanted once. It was not enough.

She has lived here for twelve years, eleven of those with him. In the early days, she was very sick, her physiology unprepared for animal germs, or human germs, or dirt in any trace amount. The smells of milk, meat and blood appalled her, as did sweat, most fluids, egg yolk, decomposing food, fungus, physical contact. Adapting to the brutal proximities of that new life, after the sterile habitation she knew as a child, was a systemic shock. Not all émigrés survived; some gave up, some went back. She was stubborn. She endured. With his help, these things became normal.

In the end, he took it well; her decision to emigrate once more, to take a further step outwards on civilisation's spectrum. After the furious disbelief, the resentment and the bitterness, came a state of resigned acceptance that both of them recognised as love. He understood that she had to go. He even helped her pack. Once he suggested accompanying her but they both knew he could not, and it was never suggested again. He is a part of this zone in a way she can never be.

Beyond the Fold, so far away they might be painted on the sky, rise the glass towers of Citadel, spectral and unreal. That is the zone where she was born, before her first emigration. There are no non-humans there, no pets, no pests, no parasites. Meat is grown in vats and the wind is ventilation. Her childhood memories are white: the fluid glide of robotic arms and hovering attentive drones, the trembling of nanomachines, the gleam of surfaces. Her parents were distant mechanisms, functional and benevolent, for whom she felt no more attachment than she did for computers. As a teenager, she gazed through UV-tinted glass at the sprawling hamlets below and dreamed of wood smoke, mud and rain. She studied hard for her escape, but only got halfway.

'I will wait for you anyway,' he says, almost to himself, 'even if you will not come back. As I wait for the rains and the newborn calves. We are waiting people.'

'And I will search for you,' she says, 'even if you will not leave. I will search for you beyond the wall. Some part of you might be there.'

He opens his mouth, closes it. There is nothing more to say. They stand together in the orange light, waiting for the wall to open and the émigrés to walk through. She strokes his hand, releases it. It has other duties now. Cutting and felling and trimming and mending and constructing and repairing. It cannot hold her any more. She must walk on alone.

There was once another conurbation here. It exists within living memory, though not for too much longer. The metropolis died from the outside in, as precarity prevailed, as the supply chains failed, as the outmost suburbs fell away, as the roads were overgrown. Pastures took the place of lawns, garages became cattle barns. It was the great unravelling and the great returning. But the city's core remained. Immutable in glass and steel, its skyscrapers like granite cones from which everything else erodes, the zone they now call Citadel, calcified at the centre. The Fold surrounds it on all sides, a messy loop of life and death. And beyond the Fold, the Rewilderness. Which is to say, the world.

This is the choice that the city gives, the choice that is her birthright. To decide what life she wants to live, what sort of human she needs to be. Out there, she will find no human rules, only the relationships of a natural world she does not know. She will learn. She will start again.

A creak. The gate swings open.

The émigrés gaze through the wall at the pulsing greenness that unfolds, shuffling for a clear view.

It is darker than she expected. The uncut shade of trees.

MERYL MCMASTER

Sentience (from the series 'In-Between Worlds')

Digital chromogenic print

The idea of 'In-Between Worlds' struck me as an opportunity to express my bi-cultural heritage, Plains Cree/British and Dutch, not as a struggle but rather as a strategic way of thinking of how they connect. I belong to two heritages, existing betwixt and between. My work explores ways of mixing and transforming these histories. Through working on this series, I intended to transform the way I view the past from the perspective of the present. (Courtesy of The Baldwin Gallery)

MOUNTAINEERS

As well as the issues shown, our seasoned Mountaineers below have also contributed to the online edition and given talks and workshops at Dark Mountain events over the last decade. Many thanks to everyone.

Akshay Ahuja grew up in New Delhi and the suburbs outside Washington, DC, and now lives in southwest Ohio with his wife and son. He works as a gardener and writes about food, plants and the arts in their wild and domesticated forms. (*Issues 3, 5, 9*)

Vanessa Andreotti is a Brazilian researcher and practitioner, examining patterns of (re)production of knowledge, inequalities and imaginaries of change. She works with the 'Gesturing Towards Decolonial Futures Collective' and the 'In Earth's CARE' network. She holds a Canada Research Chair in Race, Inequalities and Global Change at the University of British Columbia, Canada. decolonialfutures.net

Monique Besten is a visual artist and writer, born in the Netherlands and based in Barcelona but mainly at home where her feet are. In the last years her focus has been on long-distance performative walking, surviving in nature and collecting stories on the road, often in a three-piece business suit. moniquebesten.nl (*Issues 6, 9, 14*)

Kit Boyd explores our relationship with landscape in his paintings and prints. The human figure is purposefully small compared to the surrounding environment. Kit's studio overlooks the Thames Barrier, though he spends much of his time in the rolling hills of mid-Wales, a landscape that has inspired him for over 30 years. kitboyd.com (*Issues 4, 10*)

Nancy Campbell is a Literature Fellow at Internationales Künstlerhaus Villa Concordia in Bamberg, Germany. Residencies with various Arctic research institutions led to her books on the polar regions, including *The Library of Ice* and *Disko Bay*. In 2018/19, Nancy was the Canal Laureate, writing about the UK's waterways. nancycampbell.co.uk (*Issues 6, 10, 14*)

Rob Carney is the author of five books of poems, including *The Book of Sharks* (Black Lawrence Press) and *88 Maps* (Lost Horse Press). In 2014 he received the Robinson Jeffers Award for Poetry. His work has appeared in *Dark Mountain* and many other journals. He lives in Salt Lake City. (*Issue 10*)

Rebecca Chan is a filmmaker and photographer. She enjoys experimenting and collaborating with others to tell stories. She has also worked with different learning disability organisations and is interested in exploring the possibilities of film in making information accessible to everyone.

Cate Chapman is a poet and freelance editor, based in the UK. Her work has been featured in a number of print publications including *Walking on Lava* (Chelsea Green) and the forthcoming *Letters to the Earth* (HarperCollins). Cate currently works as poetry editor for the Dark Mountain Project. Twitter: @wordbird_ (*Issues 5, 6, 8, 10, 13, 15*)

Mike Cipra has lived and written in landscapes ranging from Death Valley to the old-growth redwood forests of northern California. He is honoured to be included among the writers, artists and thinkers involved in the Dark Mountain Project. mikecipra.com (*Issues 13, 15*)

Rebecca Clark is a US artist who works primarily in pencil on paper. She has exhibited in numerous galleries in the States and her work has been featured in publications such as: *Alterity Journal*, *Zoomorphic*, *Elementum Journal*, *works & conversations*, *EarthLines*, *Orion Magazine*, and *The Learned Pig*. rebeccaclarkart.com (*Issues 7, 9*)

Working primarily with found and discarded materials, **Katie Ione Craney**'s work explores the urgency of a rapidly changing northern landscape and the human and non-human response to the climate crisis. She lives in a small community in southeast Alaska, along the edge of the deepest glaciated fjord in North America. katieionecraney.com (*Issues 11, 13*)

Catrina Davies is the author of *Homesick: Why I Live in a Shed*, published by Quercus, and *The Ribbons are for Fearlessness*, published by Summersdale in the UK and Skyhorse in the US. She lives in a shed near Land's End, Cornwall, UK (*Issue 8*)

Charlotte Du Cann is a writer, performer and editor, and one of the core team behind the Dark Mountain Project. She teaches a dramaturgical writing practice called The Uneasy Chair, and writes (uneasily) about the mythology of collapse. She lives on the Suffolk coast. (*Issues 3, 6, 8, 10, 11, 13, 14*)

Rachel Economy is a facilitator, poet-performer and permaculture design educator. Her writing appears in *Dark Mountain*, *Animal*, *Dark Matter: Women Witnessing* and elsewhere. Rachel is the founder of

IndexForTheNextWorld.com, an online hub of visions for a world that thrives. 'A Home for the Seeds' was first published in *Dark Matter: Women Witnessing Issue #5*. racheleconomy.com (*Issue 11*)

David Ellingsen is a Canadian photographer creating images that speak to the relationship between humans and the natural world. Themes of witness, memory and mourning feature prominently in his work. (*Issue 14*)

Margaret Elphinstone's latest novel, *The Gathering Night,* was about Scotland's Mesolithic hunter-gatherers, and how they connected to the living world around them. In response to escalating environmental changes, she is now a climate change activist and is writing a book of essays on the theme of re-connections. (*Issue 4*)

Raquel Vasquez Gilliland is a Mexican-American poet, novelist and painter. She received her MFA in poetry from the University of Alaska, Anchorage in 2017. When not writing, Raquel tells stories to her plants and they tell her stories back. She lives in Tennessee with her beloved family and mountains. (*Issue 7*).

'Excerpt from Letter to the Ancestry Company' was originally published in *Catamaran Literary Reader*, and in Raquel's debut collection, *Dirt and Honey* (Green Writers Press).

Jay Griffiths is the author of several works of non-fiction including *Wild: An Elemental Journey* and *Kith: The Riddle of the Childscape*. She has written fiction based on the life of Frida Kahlo, and also on the anti-road protest movement. (*Issues 1, 2*)

Vinay Gupta is an environmentalist, meditator and technologist working mainly on refugee issues. He worked on nuclear and pandemic contingencies for several governments and project-managed the launch of Ethereum. In 1998, he was recognised as enlightened by his Hindu guru, and is an active member of the Nath Sampradaya. (*Issues 1, 2*)

Samantha M. Harvey is a writer and new mother living in New York City. Her work has appeared in *Grist*, *Earth Island Journal*, *Truthout* and more. She works with the Center for Diversity and the Environment and the EDGE Funders Alliance to support grassroots movements pushing for systemic change. (*Issues 5, 14*)

Nick Hayes is a writer and illustrator. He has published four graphic novels with Penguin Random House and is the chief propagandist for the Land Justice Network. He is currently finishing his first non-fiction book, in which he trespasses the country estates and ducal castles of England's land-owning magnates. (*Issue 10*)

Dougald Hine was co-author of *Uncivilisation: The Dark Mountain Manifesto* and spent ten years at the heart of the Dark Mountain Project. In July 2019, he handed on his responsibilities and he is looking forward to a rest. (*Issues 1–4, 7, 9, 12, 15*)

Some things **Harvye Hodja** has written are collected at ironriverreview.org. (*Issues 13, 14*)

Bruce Hooke is a photographer, sculptor and performance artist based in rural, western Massachusetts. Photography has been central to his artistic practice for over 15 years. His work focuses on the evolving human relationship with nature as well as on issues of gender and nature, and male power and vulnerability. bghooke.com (*Issues 9, 13, 14*)

Nick Hunt is an editor at Dark Mountain. He has also authored two travel books, *Where the Wild Winds Are* and *Walking the Woods and the Water,* and a work of gonzo ornithology, *The Parakeeting of London*. He is currently working on *Loss Soup*, a collection of short stories, and a third travel book. nickhuntscrutiny.com (*Issues 1–3, 5, 6, 9, 10, 11, 14, 15*)

Neale Inglenook lives on the California coast he grew from, along with his parents, wife and daughters. Lines of Robinson Jeffers' poetry often escape his mouth by accident. He is a contributing editor to the online edition of Dark Mountain, and his fiction and essays can be found in the pages of the print journal. digital-material.net (*Issues 6, 10, 15*)

Man Down is **Teddy Jefferson**'s second collaboration as photographer with Robert Leaver. He most frequently photographs sculpture and urban landscapes, most recently in Tunisia and Kolkata. Author of *One Inch Leather: 14 Stories*, *Rorschach Tempest* (sedizioni), and numerous stories, essays, and plays, including *The Wedding*, *The Desk*, and *The Insomniac*. (*Issue 6*)

Nicholas Kahn & Richard Selesnick are a collaborative artist team who work primarily in the fields of photography and installation art, specialising in fictitious histories set in the past or future. Kahn & Selesnick have participated in exhibitions worldwide and have work in over 20 collections. In addition, they have published three books with Aperture Press: *Scotlandfuturebog*, *City of Salt* and *Apollo Prophecies*. (*Issues 9, 13*)

Thomas Keyes is an Irish artist, forager and gardener living on the Black Isle. With a background in graffiti writing he now specialises in insular manuscript illumination and the supporting processes of traditional parchment and pigment making in an effort to understand the emergence of the alphabet. thomaskeyes.co.uk (*Issues 2, 3, 5, 8, 12*)

Paul Kingsnorth co-founded the Dark Mountain Project in 2009 and was one of its directors until 2017. He is also the author of two novels, two poetry collections and four books of non-fiction. (*Issues 1–5, 8–10*)

Anthea Lawson is an activist, writer, mother and Dark Mountain editor living in Devon near the river Dart. She has been a journalist and an NGO campaigner, and is currently writing a book called *The Entangled Activist*, to be published by Perspectiva Press. systems-souls-society.com (*Issue 13*)

Gavin Leane is a Dublin-based photographer. From an early age, he has shot an extremely wide range of subject matter, always seeking to challenge his use of method. He has exhibited at the Natural History Museum in London and, more recently, in the National Gallery of Ireland. Instagram: @orange_owl

Robert O. Leaver is a musician, writer and performance artist. His base of operations can be found on a dead-end road in the Catskill Mountains. More can be seen/read/heard at robertoleaver.com. (*Issues 6, 8, 9*)

Sylvia Linsteadt divides her time between Crete and coastal California. Her books include *The Stargold Chronicles*, a duology of environmental fantasy for middle-grade readers, the short story collection *Our Lady of the Dark Country*, and the apocalyptic folklore-cycle *Tatterdemalion*, with artist Rima Staines. sylvialinsteadt.com. (*Issues 4, 9, 12*)

Jane Lovell is an award-winning poet whose work is steeped in natural history, science and folklore. Her latest collection is *This Tilting Earth,* published by Seren. Jane also writes for *Elementum Journal.* She is currently Writer-in-Residence at Rye Harbour Nature Reserve. janelovell128.wixsite.com/janelovellpoetry (*Issues 9–11, 15*)

Sophie McKeand is a Welsh writer and poet slow-travelling across Europe with her partner and two rescue hounds. She writes about her nomadic, minimalist way of being in the world to interrogate ideas of land ownership, borders, nationalism, consumerism, activism, and the poetic imagination. sophiemckeand.com/outsider (*Issues 4, 11*)

Alastair McIntosh is a Quaker, activist and independent scholar, known for his work on human ecology, land reform, nonviolence and cultural psychotherapy. His books include *Soil and Soul: People versus Corporate Power*, *Hell and High Water: Climate Change, Hope and the Human Condition* and

Poacher's Pilgrimage: an Island Journey. (*Issues 1, 5, 8, 11*)

Artist **Meryl McMaster** explores identity through hybrid inheritances – Indigenous Canadian and European/female – with the body animated by the natural world. Her first UK solo exhibition will open at the Ikon, Birmingham in December 2019, followed by an exhibition at Canada House, London. McMaster is currently represented by The Baldwin Gallery, London.

Daniel Nakanishi-Chalwin was raised in Cornwall and now lives in Nara Prefecture in Japan. He has contributed regularly to Dark Mountain since 2015. (*Issues 7–11, 14*)

Paul O'Connor lectures in sociology at United Arab Emirates University, Abu Dhabi. His work is centred on home and community, the dynamics of modernity and globalisation, and the mediatisation and virtualisation of contemporary social life. He recently published *Home: The Foundations of Belonging* (Routledge). (*Issues 4, 8*)

Ava Osbiston explores improvisation as an expression of identity. She experiments with many different forms in her creative work. She is the production and editorial assistant for Dark Mountain and has recently set up 'Find the Others', a new strand of the Dark Mountain Project supporting readers to form discussion groups: dark-mountain.net/find-the-others/ (*Issue 8*)

Mat Osmond is based in Falmouth, Cornwall. He's currently working on a new book of poems and drawings, *The Black Madonna's Song*, a related essay about the rewilding of prayer, 'Dark River Black Light', and on helping to further the extraordinary groundswell of Extinction Rebellion within his local community and beyond. strandlinebooks.co.uk (*Issues 1, 2, 3, 7, 9, 10, 13*)

Nina Pick is a writer, teacher, editor and oral historian who, through these various practices, seeks to heal our relationship with our ancestors and the Earth. ninapick.com (*Issues 7, 10, 11, 13*)

Sarah Rea lives high in the Sierra Nevada mountains in California, where she doesn't write enough and is chastised for it. She's been polishing her edges, which isn't necessarily a good thing. Her infrequent pieces of writing can be found at copperandcoal.com. (*Issues 6, 9, 13*)

Jeri Reilly writes essays, pleas and remedial histories, her work appearing most recently in *Utne Reader*, *Dark Mountain*, *EarthLines*, and the anthology *If Bees Are Few: A Hive of Bee Poems*. She is currently completing a memoir of repair – about her 'backwards emigration' from Minnesota to a remote Irish townland. (*Issues 7, 8*)

John Rember is the author of six books, the latest of which, *100 Little Pieces on the End of the World*, will be published by the University of New Mexico Press in 2020. It contains several chapters previously published in Dark Mountain anthologies. He lives with his wife Julie in the Sawtooth Valley of Idaho. (*Issues 3–6, 11*)

Eric Robertson is a Dark Mountain editor and contributor. He teaches rhetoric and composition and environmental humanities at the University of Utah. His own published writing explores queer ecology and Geroge Bataille's concept of energy use without return, how art can help encourage human ecologies of contraction. (*Issues 4, 13*)

Caroline Ross is an artist and t'ai chi teacher living on the River Thames. She makes her tools and art materials from wild-foraging and from what other people discard. She has contributed to Dark Mountain since *Issue 8: Technê.* She teaches art and the use of wild materials in the UK and Europe. carolineross.co.uk (*Issues 8, 11, 13*)

Dr. Martin Shaw is the author of the award-winning Mythteller Trilogy (*A Branch From The Lightning Tree, Snowy Tower, Scatterlings)* and a wilderness rites of passage guide. He founded the Oral Tradition and Mythic Life courses at Stanford University and runs the Westcountry School of Myth in the UK. His new book is *The Night Wages*. (*Issue 7*)

Tom Smith is an editor at the Dark Mountain Project and a researcher in environmental studies at Masaryk University, Czech Republic. (*Issues 6, 8, 9, 13*)

Dougie Strang is a writer and performer, and member of the Dark Mountain steering group. He lives in southwest Scotland by the river Ae. dougiestrang.org (*Issues 6, 14*)

Em Strang works for Open Book and facilitates workshops in Embodied Poetry. Her first full collection, *Bird-Woman* (2016), won the 2017 Saltire Poetry Book of the Year Award. Her second collection, *Horse-Man,* is coming out in September 2019. Em's relationship with poetry is about connecting the dots between head and heart. (*Issues 3, 4, 6, 7, 9, 10*)

Both of Em's poems in this edition are reprinted with kind permission of Shearsman: 'Tog Muhoni' was originally published in *Bird-Woman* and 'Horse-Man at Crotha Bothy' in *Horse-Man*.

Kate Walters grew up near London, and always longed for wild places. Now based in Cornwall she loves to spend time in the Northern Isles. A painter, writer and newby print-maker, she's more recently a campaigner too. Obsessed

with Arctic terns; blessed to have had a horse for a mother.
Instagram: @katewaltersartist (*Issues 6, 10, 13*)

Ben Weaver is a songwriter and poet who travels by bicycle. He uses his music as a tool to strengthen relationships between people and ecosystems. Given the choice he will side with the animals, lakes, rivers and the trees. benweaver.net (*Issues 4, 13*)

Steve Wheeler is a writer, Human Rewilder and practitioner of the Daoist arts. He mostly lives in Western Europe, where he practices traditional medicine, teaches workshops, and helps to make Dark Mountain books and events. Steve doesn't believe in deadlines unless there's an actual risk of someone dying. (*Issues 2, 4, 6, 8, 11, 12, 15*)

Kate Williamson lives in a nature reserve in the South Island of New Zealand surrounded by native trees, birds and rushing water. Williamson describes herself as 'a humble cave painter trying to capture the unrivalled splendour of Nature (the real artist) on canvas' at a time when the body of Gaia, our home, is under threat of collapse. katewilliamsonart.com (*Issues 9, 13*)

DaRk MOUNTAIN
MAIL ORDER

Back issues in print

Walking On Lava
Selected Works for Uncivilised Times
(2017)
US paperback
£15.99

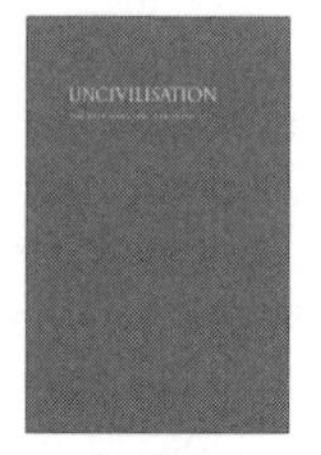

Uncivilisation
The Dark Mountain manifesto (2009)
Revised paperback ed.
£5.99

issue fifteen
(Spring 2019)
hardback
£16.99

All back issues available as pdf downloads *from £3.00 ea.*

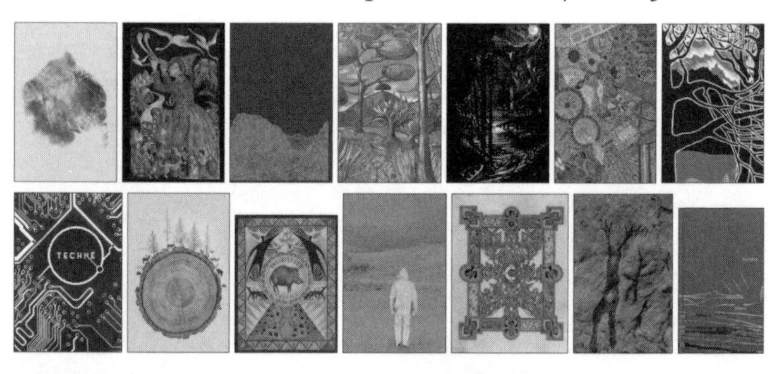

From the Mourning of the World
The first Dark Mountain LP (2013)
12 inch vinyl £14
Download £10

{Reading the Ashes}
The second Dark Mountain LP (2015)
Download £7

Also available guest publications from the Dark Mountain team please visit: dark-mountain.net/shop

ROLL OF HONOUR

The publication of this book is made possible by the support of subscribers to the Dark Mountain Project. The following subscribers have provided financial support beyond the call of duty. We are very grateful for their belief in our work, and for that of all our subscribers across the world.

Bob Archer
Keith Badger
Kay and Wahhab Baldwin
Susan Bates
Jeff Blackburn
Paula Boyle
Bruce Campbell
Sandra Carey
Ben Carpenter
Theo Clarke
Christine Crosbie
Peter Culp
Kate Davis
Brook Dickson and Kurt Navratil
Simeon Gallu
Jack Gates-Browne
Lorien Goodale
Alexander Grant
Jan Ernst de Groot
Christopher Hall
Colin Harper
James Heal
Rebecca Henderson
Victoria Hill
Ann Hine
Henrietta Hitchings
Rachel Holstead
Nathaniel Holdsworth
Michael Hughes
Andrew Hurley
Cat Ingrams
Atlantis Johnson
William Johnson
Howard Jones
Andrew Junius
Max Kloosterman
Shabehram Lohrasbe
Jennifer Loewen
Deirdre McAdams
Ian McCleave
Peter McDonald
William Maxwell
Johan Meylaerts
Brian Midtbo
Todd Moore
Stephen Nally
Matthew Osmond
S. Nate Pochan
Simon de Quincey
Johnny Rath
Gene Ray
Bonnitta Roy
Helen Sieroda
Anaiya Sophia
Susie Unseld
Celia Fulton Walden
Elizabeth Watson
Gregory Webster
Jacob Williams
Julia Winiarski
John W. Wolf
Robin Zykin